Don't Blame the Mirror

Don't Blame the Mirror

by
VIRGINIA GRAHAM

with
JEAN LIBMAN BLOCK

MEREDITH PRESS   New York

32513

Library of Congress Catalog Card Number: 67–20853

MANUFACTURED IN THE UNITED STATES OF AMERICA

Contents

v

Contents

Prologue

This is a beauty book with a four-word message. The message is: Don't blame the mirror. The mirror hanging on the wall is innocent. If anyone is guilty, you are. Your guilt may lie in indifference, in carelessness, in lack of self-concern, in misplaced emphasis. You may say you are too busy for beauty, too tired, too old, too late, or too plain.

I can't accept those excuses—not today when advice is immediately available no matter where you live, techniques are simple and sure, products are close to foolproof, and the range of beauty is unlimited. Perhaps you could not have made the highly specialized grade as a Gibson Girl. Maybe you never had it in you to be a successful flapper; you had no choice but to sit out the Jean Harlow or Marilyn Monroe eras.

But today there are no boundaries to beauty. From Barbra Streisand to Elizabeth Taylor, from Julie Christie to Joan Crawford, from Jacqueline Kennedy to Princess Margaret—there is no one type, no single size, no special age, no particular arrangement of features, no stereotype of coloring that is labeled in capital letters: BEAUTY.

Beauty is potentially in all of us. You can start anywhere, with any apparently unpromising collection of features, and achieve beauty. How do you start? Well, you've already made a beginning if you've gotten this far.

Before you read one line farther, I want to tell you that this is a different kind of beauty book. It is probably the first beauty book that really levels with women. Jean, will you explain what we mean by leveling with women?

Jean: I remember, Virginia, you used that phrase when you told me about your very first experience in the beauty business, more than twenty-five years ago, when you were the emcee of the International Beauty Show. You said yourself that you were horrified at how outspoken you were on the platform.

Virginia: That's right. I told those girls—those beauticians from beauty parlors all over the country—what was wrong with them and how to shape up and how to practice their trade on themselves before they tried to sell techniques and products to customers. I still can't get over the fact that they weren't furious at me for my blunt approach.

Jean: That's because you really leveled with them. They could feel your affection for them, your respect for their knowledge. They knew you weren't talking down to them or belittling them in any way. Some of the medicine you gave was bitter to swallow. But they knew it was right for them.

Virginia: So they made awful faces and gulped—and thanked me afterward. And I've been in the beauty business in one way or another ever since, telling women face to face, on radio, and on TV how to think about themselves, how to use their assets, how to look better.

Jean: And it's high time you put it all down in a book.

Virginia: People ask me if I'm writing this book for any special age group. After all, I'm one of the Lydia Pinkham rejects, myself. So they say, "What do you know about youthful beauty?" Well, listen, I have a memory and I have eyes. I think I have jealous eyes. Maturity gives us jealous eyes. We look with jealousy on the younger woman because she doesn't know as much now as we do, and, oh, what we could do with our wisdom and her face.

As for husbands, you may have to make up with yours after you've tried some of the things we suggest. This book is designed to bring happiness to the husband who is living so much with cosmetic beauty that the morning after he's astonished at what his wife really looks like. We're offering a little insight into the day before.

Beauty is such a transient thing. I've seen the most gorgeous six-month-old baby grow up to be the most ungainly child of fourteen. So many girls whom I knew when I was younger and who were really unattractive I met years later at parties and they hadn't changed one bit. They were still losers.

Yet others, who were ugly ducklings in their youth, have since become terribly chic, found a style for themselves, dressed in a distinctive way, perhaps arranged their hair in a stark manner that a raving beauty couldn't because the raving beauty may have tiny lines in her face. (You know all of us, at some time in our lives, are going to look like an Esso road map.) Yet the character and the individuality these women have developed mark them as far better looking than the born beauty.

With these thoughts in mind, and with the reminder that Pandora's curiosity gave her an extra wrinkle, we're here to tell you that you can't open a beauty book that is going to say to you, "Madam, your large nose is suddenly going to shrink. Your eyes, which are looking directly at each other, are now going to become straight and wide-set. Your skin, which is in the beige family, is now going to become camellialike." Don't deceive yourself into thinking you look like someone you're not. Be honest in recognizing your age, your limitations, your potentialities. What we're trying to tell you to do is not to be frantic about anything. People who are frantic about their makeup, frantic about their diet, frantic about the PTA, are the biggest social bores in the world. Their faces begin to get lines. Their voices become strident and raspy. They have a harassed look about them. And they are not easy to be with.

Not only is a tense woman a social bore, but you find yourself tightening up when you are with her. Even though this tense, tight woman may command attention for a few minutes when she comes into the room, people soon leave her because they find themselves tightening up too. You who have pleasantness and sweetness will radiate such appeal that your beauty will be far more lasting.

There is a desire in every woman to look her best. She has a compelling need to fulfill herself as a personality. Her looks are part of that fulfillment. Yet the woman of today, whether or not she has a career, has a very busy schedule. I use quite a bit of makeup, but I've gotten the routine down to the point where it takes me only seven to ten minutes to put on a full formal makeup. Any woman who can bake a cake well, or run a home, or even drive a car can organize her appearance. I think after a certain age there is no such thing as a great natural beauty. Yet there are some women who require fewer cosmetics than others. It isn't what makeup you use as much as how you apply it that helps toward the self-assurance you get from looking your best.

None of us will look like Elizabeth Taylor unless we go in for extensive plastic surgery. If a strong eyeliner and heavy eyelashes are becoming to her, there has to be a good deal of similarity between your face and hers for you to borrow her specific techniques without looking grotesque.

It is not expensive to look well and it does not take time over the long run. In the beginning, yes, when you are learning new techniques and habits, you may need a little time before the gestures become automatic. But once you have developed a routine, you will be amazed at how much you can accomplish in seconds and minutes. Just think of the first time you ever made coffee in a percolator. I bet it took you a full ten minutes to measure the water and the coffee and assemble all the parts of the pot in proper order. And then you stood there nervously to see whether the thing would ever start to perk. But now you can throw together the best pot of coffee on your block in ten seconds flat, and you don't have to be more than half awake. You'll find that practice makes for the same speed and certainty once you get accustomed to applying makeup or false eyelashes.

So "Don't blame the mirror" means face the facts. Then alter the facts if you don't like them. It's not going to cost you much money. It will cost you personal truthfulness, seriousness of intent, and better scheduling of the time which you may be squandering. Beauty that isn't developed is fruitful acreage lost forever. We feel that every year can bring its compensations and it's up to you to develop them. This can start at the age of eighteen or eighty. There is no correct age to begin—except now.

No, you don't have to buy five creams and apply them in mysterious sequence to get results. Of course if you want your husband to slide out of bed with a broken neck, that's one way of doing it. Frankly, I think that unless night creams are completely invisible, the husband will vanish sooner than the wrinkles.

If you're busy during the day, when will you save your face? You can put on a cream when you are getting into a hot bath and give perhaps five minutes more to your bath. You'll get as much saturation as you would from sleeping all night in a fine coating of grease.

Sometimes I wake up in the morning looking like Halloween is over, but why didn't someone tell me? But I put my makeup on right away, meet the day, and find I am able to do things on arising that I thought I never could. I always say I don't mind if women are two-faced provided they don't go out with the face they woke up with. I disagree with anyone who thinks there is too much vanity or conceit in the art of being well made-up and perfectly coiffed. The most conceited woman in the world is the one who feels God made her pretty enough so that she needs no help.

If you still hope there is an Open Sesame to beauty, let me tell you there isn't. I really found out what glorious hoaxes can exist in the world of beauty when I was very young and read about a cold cream that opened the pores, cleansed the pores, nourished the pores, and closed the pores. I asked my father, to whom I went for everything, "How is it done, Papa? How can a cream in a jar be so smart?"

"I don't think the cream is so smart," he said, "but I guess the man who sells the cream is very smart." Yes, the promise is ridiculous. But for many women the need to hope is so great that it exceeds the promise in foolishness.

Beauty is an illusion. It is also a disillusion. I've heard that some countries have a law that says a man must see how his future bride looks the first thing in the morning so that later their marriage would not be annulled for misrepresentation.

No honey or elixir from a bee that flies over Africa at a certain time of the year or a flower that spews rare pollen will rejuvenate you. There are no secret things. But there are things that are no longer kept secret.

I get phone calls from Mama, who at eighty is still one of the most beautiful women in Chicago, and she may say to me: "Dear, I've been reading what so-and-so says, and she owes her skin completely to lemon."

I say, "How appealing," but the pun is lost on Mama.

She says, "You squeeze a little lemon on your face."

I say, "Tell me, where do you put the tea bag? It sounds like a marvelous drink."

"I'm telling you," Mama says, "that's what she does. That's why she's beautiful."

So even people who know better want a magic formula. Well, if you want magic, stop reading this book and go back to looking dreadful. But if you want a simple, normal, natural way to look your best all day, every day, then *don't blame the mirror!*

Don't Blame the Mirror

1

What Is Beauty?

Beauty, according to the *American College Dictionary,* is that quality of any object or sense or thought which excites an admiring pleasure; qualification of a high order for delighting the eye or the esthetic, intellectual, or moral sense; something beautiful, especially a woman, a grace, a charm, or a pleasing excellence is beauty. A synonym for beauty is loveliness.

For beautiful, which is the adjective, the dictionary says: Something that is lovely and pretty, and it refers to a pleasing appearance. Pretty implies a moderate but noticeable beauty, especially if it is small or of minor importance—a pretty child.

Notice that at no time is beauty defined as perfection of features or symmetry of features or enormous eyes or a lovely mouth. Beauty is something pleasing to the eye. And therefore anybody can be beautiful.

For purposes of this book I am going to define beauty as the total image of a woman, her attitude toward herself, her impact on those around her. Elements of beauty are face, figure, hair, vitality, makeup, clothes, a sense of style, enthusiasm, and above all, the way a woman feels about herself. There is no magic shortcut to give yourself an overwhelming beauty that nature never intended, but there is a way to make yourself, through shadow and lighting and skill and self-knowledge, the most attractive person you could possibly be.

Recently I talked with Bette Davis on my television program, "Girl Talk." She has so much vitality and energy that she absolutely exudes a personal beauty from her inner excitement. She is not young or beautiful by contemporary standards, yet when she walked off the stage she got more applause than any star we've ever had except, perhaps, Joan Crawford or Constance Bennett. We've had the young fabulous starlets and the screaming teen-agers on the program, yet Bette got the greatest acclaim from an audience that had waited quite a while in the rain to see her. I said to her after the program, "Aren't you lucky that you didn't relegate yourself to the category of the unchanging glamour girl."

She said, "I never did go for that type of role."

"But, Bette, you brought glamour to every role."

So I tried to figure out this word *glamour*. And I decided it is a self-confidence, an interest in other people, a tremendous excitement about life, a vitality, an awareness of a world other than your own. It is all of these—not lipstick, not rouge, not the style of your hair. It is being on top of everything. Above all, a really glamorous person is someone who has used everything life has to offer. Perhaps in your case there is an inner radiance that is being hidden by your self-consciousness, or by your lack of desire to be the focal point of all eyes. When I watch women in conventional attire, drab-colored hair and drab-colored faces, I see human chameleons who are praying that they will blend in with the background and not be noticed.

The self-confidence that gives us a sense of beauty starts very early. That is why I beseech and beg mothers, grandmothers, and anyone else who is close to a little child, to tell that child over and over, "Oh, you're so lovely. Look how sweet the baby looks." My mother's strict background always made her say that vanity was an evil.

Once I saw a sign on a billboard in Springfield, Illinois, "Love thyself and thou wilt hate thy neighbor." But this is an absolute fallacy. If you do not love yourself, you cannot love anybody else or expect them to love you. When you are around a little child, do not try to attain perfection by tearing down. Give the child love. Tell the little girl how sweet she is. Have her take pride in clean, glistening hair from childhood; perhaps a little bubble bath in her tub, to make her aware of body fragrance. One of the great qualities of glamour is radiance. We are trying to give people a reverence for radiance. Yet radiance is not a cosmetic—it is a point of view. It is a mental attitude that permeates every action.

So how do you as an adult get self-confidence and radiance? You look at yourself, straight ahead in the mirror—not at the woman sitting next to you or anybody else—and you say, "Look, this is it. What am I going to do about it?"

JEAN: You know, Virginia, as you were talking about the way to treat a little child, I was thinking of the documentary film, *The Eleanor Roosevelt Story*. You know, she was the saddest little girl. Her parents had died when she was very young and she was completely alone. There was one heartbreaking photograph of her and her cousins at their grandmother's country place. While all the other youngsters were engaged in a ballgame, there was Eleanor, sitting in a forlorn heap on the grass, all alone, looking shyly at the others. From the day she was born she was told she was homely. The old photographs of her as a teen-ager show her awkward, gawky, and self-conscious. She looked as if she might burst into tears at any moment. But then, an hour later, as her life unfolds on the screen, you see her as a magnificent woman in her later years—poised, gracious, radiant. Eleanor Roosevelt achieved, with time, a special beauty of her own.

VIRGINIA: What do you suppose gave her this later radiance?

JEAN: I think from the beginning this woman had a strength within her that was deeply hidden, as it is in many of us. From an underprivileged childhood—a childhood with all the money in the world, but no love—she had to grope her way to find herself as a person. In her life it was tragedy that made the difference. She was so submissive and dutiful and unsure of herself that even after her five children were born her mother-in-law was still ordering all the food for her household and making every decision that a wife should make for herself. But at the time of Franklin Roosevelt's illness, when he was paralyzed, she took a stand. His mother tucked him into his wheelchair and said, in effect, "All right, dear boy, you take it easy; we'll take care of you now." But Eleanor said, *"No, we're not going to take care of you. You're going to go out and take care of us."*

6

The film may have overdramatized the struggle between these two women for a great man's soul, but the struggle must have existed. The submissive, passive Eleanor fought her mother-in-law, and to some extent fought her husband, for he was unsure of what he wanted to do. Once he decided to reenter the world, she became his eyes and ears. She met the people of the world. And from the deep reservoir of her own suffering she reached out to them. The light within her became reflected in her face.

VIRGINIA: I like that—the light within her became reflected in her face. Tell me, Jean, what makes you notice a woman when she walks into a room? What do you mean when you say she's beautifully groomed?

JEAN: It's the perfection of detail, that all-in-one-piece, the everything-goes-together look that appears effortless, but of course isn't, and that most women find so difficult to achieve. Everything she has on is inevitably right. And you know by looking at her that her closet is organized, her wardrobe is organized, she has everything in perfect repair, and she knows exactly where everything is.

VIRGINIA: A real test of a beautiful woman is that you never see one thing about her that really stands out. You see her whole. Her appearance shouldn't invite you to say, "Darling, your makeup is stunning," or "What extraordinary gloves." The other day I saw a young girl in a solid navy jersey dress, without even a single pearl, not an earring, nothing—except bright, lipstick-red, shiny patent leather shoes. All you could remember about that girl was the red of her shoes. I suppose this may be all right for a youngster who is out to achieve a kooky look. But I definitely don't think it's for her older sisters or for her mother. Of course, if a woman's legs are her best feature and the rest of her is undistinguished, she will play them up so that they don't go unnoticed; but I don't think she should walk around with a spotlight on her legs. The total effect becomes grotesque.

Your dress has to be pressed. It has to be spotless. I can't overemphasize the pressing of clothes, spot cleaning, checking hems, making sure your shoulder strap never slips, seeing to it that your gloves are smudgeless. Harry and I play this game a million times. We watch women walking down the street. He says to me, "Doesn't she look great? She looks so clean and fresh." This can be every woman's beauty.

All this is a question of self-respect. I always go back to the woman who throws up her hands and says, "Who has the time?" She claims that all the impeccable little details are for someone else. She never has the time. Or the money. But I feel that here we are really dealing with self-respect. For a woman must feel that she owes a certain part of each day to herself. She must realize that she has the right to take the time from all the obligations that are pressing in on her to devote at least a few minutes every day to herself and her beauty needs.

Have you ever wondered about the person who invented the mirror? I've had it in for him ever since I was a child. It's bad enough if you're not beautiful, but why do you have to be constantly reminded of it? I've always been baffled by the legend of Narcissus and the notion that anyone could be in love with his own image. I've thought, How wonderful to be either myopic or far-sighted. Twenty-twenty vision can be a terrible handicap because you have to live with a clear image in the mirror and not with a friendly blur you can pretend is somebody else.

Phyllis Diller, one of the funniest women I've ever known, never looks at herself until noon. She has no mirrors in her bedroom. She starts at about lunchtime with a compact mirror to find out if her eyes are open, and by five she might take a peek from the neck up. I've looked at myself in the morning when everything is hanging—I mean everything. I think I have a house guest. I cannot believe that this is I. But when you walk from one room to another, and the same face goes with you, you can't blame the mirror any longer.

You have to figure out what to do about yourself.

2

Don't Think You're
the Only One

Everybody's busy today—with a job, a baby, a household, a Red Cross project, an ailing mother-in-law. They say women are more leisured than ever before, but I don't see it when I look around among my friends. Even those who have no outside jobs and who have help in the house become so caught up in their charities or their complex social lives that you can only make a date with them three weeks in advance. If I want to have lunch with a woman on the spur of the moment, do you know what I do? I call up someone I know with a fulltime office job. She's more likely to be available than a country club type who couldn't possibly squeeze me in between her fitting and her facial.

When does the busy woman have time for beauty? I'm going to start by talking about myself. And first I want to tell you how busy I really am.

It's true I have a maid, but I am a compulsive cleaner and I am constantly, constantly working around the house. My day starts at eight o'clock, no matter what time I go to bed. There are household repairs, marketing to do, letters to write, my daughter Lynn's needs, things to do for my two grandchildren, charities that I'm interested in, many meetings each week, a weekly beauty parlor appointment and sometimes comb-outs in between, taping of "Girl Talk" on Thursdays and Fridays from four to eight P.M., personal appearance trips to distant cities for Clairol several times a month, a column I write for a Clairol publication that goes to beauticians, guest appearances on TV and radio shows, this book I've been writing, the earlier book, my life story, *There Goes What's Her Name*. I truly think I am the busiest person I know. But I do have a beauty schedule.

My schedule is based on the fact that I don't believe in using creams and oils for longer than five minutes. I feel that all the good that will be done on the skin by creams and oils can be done quickly. I don't believe there is a woman in the world who can't take a half hour for beauty during her bath period. While she is getting ready for her bath she can put a cleansing cream on her face. Now I don't go in for all these things that other people are talking about. I've looked at turtles and found them the oldest looking creatures in the world. I don't think that sheep look so young. So when they start giving me the hormones and the oils from all these elderly looking animals, I don't buy it. I use a cream that my grandmother used. It's a cleansing cream for dry skin. I put it on my face while I'm brushing my teeth and the bath water is running. I prefer a bath to a shower because this is my luxuriating period. As the warm vapors rise from the tub, the extra moisture in the air helps the cream on my face do its work. If the phone rings while I'm in the tub and I'm alone in the house, it can ring forever. I won't get out of the tub to answer it. (Of course while I'm in the tub I'm looking at a spot on the wall that needs cleaning and wondering how soon I'll have to replace the wallpaper.) When I get out of the tub, I remove the cream from my face.

That's my beauty time, and I believe every woman deserves equal time. No woman should feel guilty about taking time out from things she thinks she should be doing—mending socks, polishing silver—to do things solely for herself. She asks, who am I, and why should I concentrate on me? I feel there is a lack of healthy ego and essential love of self, if out of a twenty-four-hour day you are afraid to insist that a half hour of it really belongs to you.

JEAN: I have a thought for the busy woman. You know, the average bathroom simply doesn't have room for all the things she needs. The ordinary medicine cabinets overflow in no time. When I moved from a large house to a much smaller apartment, I took the bookcase part of an old secretary, with two glass doors, and had it hung on a wall in the bathroom. I painted it white, lined it with the bathroom wallpaper, and had the glass in the doors replaced with mirrors. It gave me enormous private shelf space for everything.

VIRGINIA: You're recommending to women the economy of effort involved in having everything—soaps, lotions, creams, spray, reserve tissues—right where they're needed. Tell me, what do you do with makeup brushes and pencils? I stand mine up in little mayonnaise jars.

JEAN: I use a soup mug. One thing—if you stand up brushes, please, please be careful to put them away handle down. You don't want the weight of the brush to rest on the delicately pointed sable tip.

VIRGINIA: My daughter Lynn did something very clever, and it cost her almost nothing. A couple of her husband's friends got together over the weekend, and built and wallpapered a cabinet that encloses the space under the basin. It's a marvelous utility cabinet.

The hurried woman should have a little shelf right near the bathtub, or perhaps behind the shower curtain, where she keeps her hair spray, the detergent and sponge which she uses to swish out the tub after bathing so she doesn't have to waste a lot of time scrubbing it, and her oil or cream and lotion.

Another thing, your hair rollers and bobby pins and the chiffon scarves you wear over the rollers should be right in the bathroom, so that if you're in a hurry you can put up your hair during the couple of minutes your bath is running.

Talking about saving time, there is one shortcut I simply don't get. What's with the women who wear hair rollers in public? You know, if I could leave to this world one single gift, it would be the elimination of the public hair roller. Women do not even wear scarves over the rollers. They use those big, pink perforated plastic rollers that look like a ruptured appendix. I see women wearing these rollers out with their husbands in cars and in all sorts of public places. Do women have any idea of how unbecoming the rollers are and how ghastly they look with those fat sausage arrangements in their hair? I just don't understand it.

13

JEAN: I interviewed Gregory Peck's wife recently, a most charming French woman. She said that she was baffled by American women and their hair rollers and she wondered when they ever took the rollers out.

VIRGINIA: She's right—I don't think some of them ever take the rollers out. That's their hair style: At the Merv Griffin show one night when I was doing a guest appearance I noticed a woman in the front row who was wearing overstuffed rollers in her hair. Usually on this show the audience asks the guests questions. But I decided to turn the thing around. I said to her, "Madam, I have a question. Here you are in a theater in midtown Manhattan at a television broadcast—an event for which you planned and dressed and came downtown. But you have rollers in your hair. When do you expect to take them out?" Jack E. Leonard was on the panel that night and he yelled, "She's going to the opera later." We all got hysterical and there never was any answer from that woman.

I just don't get what it is with the rollers in public. I think the women who wear them should be forced to take a good, hard look at themselves in the mirror. And then they should go to a store and buy one of the adorable eyelet or ruched nylon net caps made to wear over rollers. My daughter Lynn has a ruffled organza clown cap she puts on over her curlers and it's one of the most becoming headdresses she owns.

You know, one of these days I'd like to open "Girl Talk" with three of our great beauties wearing their hair up in rollers. The trouble is that girls who are really beautiful and who care about their looks wouldn't be caught dead with rollers—even for the purpose of teaching other women a lesson. Our only hope is that one day soon there will be a revolt of husbands and

14

boy friends. Men of America, arise! Assert your rights. Put an end to rollers in public!

Now that I've gotten that off my chest, I'd like to tell you about a special habit I find very useful for my way of life. The minute I get into the house after being out during the day, I take all my clothes off and get into a robe. Even if I have to go out again two hours later, I still take off everything, put on a robe, and stretch out on my bed. I don't necessarily go to sleep. I may be opening mail, or talking on the telephone, or going over bills. But from the minute I'm home in the afternoon—and this goes for evenings, too—I wear a robe. I think in the first place it saves wear and tear on clothes. Second, I like the way I look and feel in a floor-length robe. I always buy full-length robes—I can't stand a long gown hanging out from under a robe. Of course, we all have what I call a shaggy dog robe—a messy old friend of a robe that we might even wear into bed when we have a cold or chill. But if we have any sense, even if we've been married a thousand years, we don't let our husbands see us in that.

My advice to women is to get into a robe. It can be an inexpensive nylon print that you can get for next to nothing and drip-dry on a hanger, or an amusing shift with one of those big industrial zippers. Whatever your choice, let your robe be your best friend.

JEAN: I'll try to take your advice, but I'm afraid, Virginia, that I'm not a robe person. I wish I were. I have friends who have marvelous wardrobes of robes and get more use out of them than out of their clothes. But I haven't been able to pick up the robe habit, though I've tried. I once bought a floor-length, black velvet hostess gown. It was so good-looking that I wore

15

it as a dinner dress instead of as a robe. But I'm not comfortable with myself unless I stay fully dressed, and that includes stockings, bra, girdle—everything—until I'm ready to climb into bed for the night. I'm afraid I don't have a robe personality.

VIRGINIA: One of the television programs I used to get a kick out of was Art Linkletter's when he tried to find out what women carried in their purses. He gave prizes for the most outrageous things that tumbled out when women turned their purses upside down. But seriously, what beauty items should a busy woman carry? Certainly a compact, an eyebrow pencil, a lipstick, a lipstick brush, if you're the type who likes to apply lipstick with a brush; rouge, in case your face pales; a tiny tube of cleansing cream; and if you regularly use eyeliner and mascara, these too should be in your purse. You know that a little bit of eyeshadow can transform a daytime shopping face to a nighttime supper club face. All you have to do is to go into a ladies' room, and very quietly you can redo your whole face. You might want to carry a couple of those little wash-and-dry packets. They're wonderful for a quick makeup change if you're not a cream user.

These essential items should all be in a little case or zipper bag which you can quickly transfer from one purse to another. The case saves the lining of your purse from lipstick or pencil stains and avoids the calamity you face when you discover that in hurriedly switching from your blue to your brown bag you inadvertently left the lipstick behind. That's really the worst feeling—to be caught out without a lipstick. It invariably happens when every store for miles around is closed, and you have to choose between going lipstickless or asking a stranger if you can borrow hers.

16

Another thing the smart woman carries is a plastic rain hood and a fresh pair of washable gloves, and even an extra pair of stockings. If you're about to tell me that you'll need a bag as big as a suitcase for all this equipment, I suggest you take a look at the fashion magazines or at the expensive bag department in your local store. You'll see that the smart daytime bag is generously sized for the very reason that the busy, well-dressed, well-groomed woman needs a lot of portable carrying space.

If you're busy, you must reduce maintenance time for your wardrobe to a minimum. You are certainly aware of the nylon world, the drip-dry world, the color-fast world, the crease-resistant world. There is a message the manufacturer is trying to get to you. He is saying: "Madam, this is how you should look, and we're trying to make it quick and easy for you."

If a dress has collar and cuffs that constantly need washing and ironing, if a suit has a blouse that is always at the dry cleaner's, replace the parts that require heavy upkeep with items that need only a swish through the suds to dry crisp and pretty. The day is long past when synthetics looked like leftovers from a rummage sale. Use them whenever you can, with gratitude that technology has offered you the gift of time.

Clear the stuff you don't use out of your closets and drawers. If you can't bear to throw things away, at least banish what you are not wearing at the moment to the attic or to a big box at the top of your closet. When your closet is overcrowded, you are forced to waste time looking for what you want and then pressing dresses and suits that had no room to hang freely.

Organize your accessories on some practical basis. I do it by seasons—summer, winter, and in-between things kept together. You may want to do it by color. I have a friend who puts the

17

gloves she wears with a particular bag inside that bag between wearings.

Try to arrange not to keep your lingerie in a big, deep drawer. When you grope down toward the bottom for a strapless black bra, you're likely to snarl everything else into a tangle. Shallow drawers are best for underthings—remember that if you're refurnishing or are in the market for a bureau. Maybe your husband or son or the handyman can build dividers into your big drawers so you can keep related items together.

Sewing things should always be near the surface. You should never skip tightening a button or repairing a strap because the scissors are temporarily lost or the right color thread isn't around. There's much to be said for our grandmothers' custom of keeping a decorative little cushion on the dresser with needles already threaded with black, white, and perhaps beige thread. Instant small repairs will save considerable time and money in the long run. Have you discovered sewing glue, which you can get in tubes in the Five-and-Ten? It lets you repair a hem in one minute flat. A roll of Scotch tape should always be at hand; it, too, can save a hem or temporarily restore a tear from the inside.

Above all, don't think about all the things you have to do. If I stopped to think about the countless dates and deadlines and obligations on my schedule, I'd be paralyzed. I wouldn't get one single thing done. My secret is to do things like a recovering alcoholic—day by day. I have never allowed life to seem unconquerable. I do this by living each cycle of twenty-four hours. I think you should do the same thing. And no matter how busy you are—with the Scouts, with the PTA, with your job—you must still take a half hour for yourself. And you must take it every day.

18

3

Mirror, Mirror, on the Wall

I hesitate to tell you exactly what my skin-care routine is, for I don't want you to go out and try the identical thing and then complain that it doesn't work for you. My shoes won't fit you, so why should my beauty procedures? I can't overemphasize the point that you must not copy me, or a big film star, or the woman next door. My skin, for example, holds powder and makeup without a foundation or base. People won't believe me when I tell them I never use a base—not even for TV. The texture of my skin is such that powder, rouge, even powder eyeshadow, cling for hours. *Your* skin may be such that without a good strong base that conceals tiny blemishes and evens out color variations and freckles, your makeup looks simply terrible.

I think when you grasp the whole range of variations in makeup you will have taken an important step in achieving beauty. You will have opened your mind to the infinite variety of possibilities—some of which will be great for you and others utterly deplorable.

Sometimes, you know, the women you think wear the least makeup really wear the most. And those who don't know how to put it on look overly made-up, even if they're just wearing a dab of eyeshadow and lipstick. Now if any one part of your makeup calls attention to itself—it's wrong. Lots of young girls today have that no-lipstick look which makes them resemble an embalmer's practice session. No lipstick stands out far more than a natural pink lipstick. Then, to give their skin any color at all, they put on too much rouge.

Do you know there are models who have their back teeth pulled out to get sunken hollows in their cheeks? Those girls aren't happy unless they look like cadavers.

I remember when I was a young girl, before I went to bed, I took off all my makeup and then I put a little bit of powder on my nose and just a touch of lipstick. My roommate at school used to look at me and say, "Some day you're going to pay for this. You'll ruin your skin." I'd say, "Well, you never know whom you're going to meet in your dreams."

I'd advise the newlywed to use just a little dusting of powder on the nose at night. It's an amazing thing—you don't really need any other makeup because just a touch of powder on the nose will soften your looks. I realize there's a whole new group of people today who don't like powder and don't like the pow-

20

dered look. But I feel that other than the rare, rare beauty, there isn't a person I know who doesn't look prettier with a powdered look.

JEAN: You know, Virginia, many women today are using a transparent finishing powder that gives a powdered effect without adding any color to the skin or the foundation. They like it because it prevents that yellow-orange look that sometimes results from many coats of powder on a fairly oily skin or oily base.

VIRGINIA: That's all right. But suppose you want a pink look?

JEAN: You get the color either from your normal skin tones or from the foundation. I don't think many women these days are relying on powder alone to provide color. Another way to get the powdered look and the warmer skin tone is by brushing on one of the new blushers. They're very effective, not just for highlighting the cheeks, but for giving an all-over glow to the face and throat.

VIRGINIA: Let's talk about wrinkles. I believe a good cream —and there are many of them—will give you needed surface moisture and lubrication. I do not believe there is any cream that will get rid of wrinkles. A good oiling of the skin as you go along will prevent wrinkles from forming, but once they're there, I've never seen a cream that will remove them.

You know, as conscious as I am about most things connected with beauty, I never paid much attention to my elbows until one day, visiting a friend in the hospital, I noticed how red and wrinkled her elbows were. I couldn't get over how terribly ugly elbows can be if they're not taken care of. Elbows have to be oiled or creamed every time you get out of the bath.

JEAN: That reminds me of an interview I read recently of a girl who is one of the top hand models. You see her hands in advertisements in magazines and on television. They are the most beautiful hands you ever saw, with nails like jewels. She told the interviewer that she has several children and does housework. To protect her hands she wears little cotton gloves most of the time and keeps bottles of lotion all over. Visitors fall over lotion in her apartment, and every time she lifts a pin with her hands, she reapplies lotion.

VIRGINIA: Jean, that's the most boring and deadliest thing I've ever heard in my life. I suppose if she makes a living from her hands, this model has to make her whole world revolve around them. But are you suggesting that the average woman is going to worry about lotion in every room?

JEAN: No, because the average woman doesn't have to be that involved with her hands, but the point I want to make is that I don't think the model is in torture because of the ever-present need to keep her hands lubricated. Her routine becomes second nature to her and she automatically goes through certain motions. And that's what I think the average woman can do— on a lesser scale, of course. She can keep the lotion in the bathroom, near the kitchen sink, and on her dressing table.

VIRGINIA: Dressing table! You're not serious! How many women do you suppose have dressing tables?

JEAN: I think nearly every woman has a place on her dresser or bureau where she keeps a few perfume bottles and maybe some pretty lipstick cases.

VIRGINIA: If you want to be practical then, why don't you put the bottle of lotion right on the floor under the bed. That's what I do. Then, while Harry's reading the paper, and I'm stretched out glancing at a book, I give myself the hand test. If I find I've gotten roughed up, I reach right under the bed where I've secreted my little bottle.

One thing I deplore is the no-nail-polish look. You have no nail polish, Jean. Why is that?

JEAN: I always wear nail polish for dress-up occasions. But I don't wear it regularly because I have very fragile nails that split and break and refuse to hold polish for more than a day or two. When I'm busy I can't redo my nails every other day; so to avoid a chipping, peeling look, I just skip polish most of the time. I'll be perfectly frank and tell you that I've been told repeatedly by beauticians, manicurists, and even by the cosmetic chemists who make nail polish, that my nails would be in better condition if I kept them polished all the time. But my own experience over many years has convinced me that this is not so. Some people say that nails are too hard to absorb oils or nutrients from the outside, but I've found that the only way to keep my nails in any shape at all in the winter is to keep them without polish and to oil the nails and the cuticle constantly.

VIRGINIA: May I ask you this—how are your toenails?

JEAN: I can't say I think about them very often, but they don't give me any trouble, if that's what you mean.

VIRGINIA: Then I say your problem has nothing to do with your nails, but with the way you use your hands. Let me tell you, I used to go to the doctor about my nails. They broke and were peeling; there was no way I could grow a nail. Since I've been in the professional world I've learned about artificial nails, called patti-nails—a plastic nail that you have put on by a professional. I've worn them for ten years now, and my nails have all grown out. But I keep the plastic over them anyway because I get a more beautiful long oval, and the polish shows up better. Most people, I realize, don't want to go to all that trouble. But I've learned that by using my hands properly, I can keep my nails intact. I clean bathtubs and wash woodwork and I don't want women to say, "Oh, brother, if she had to do what I do!" —I don't have to do it, but I do it anyway. I guess I was raised that way. But I've learned to work with the balls of my fingers. If you learn to do that, you can prevent a lot of nail breakage. Besides, Jean, there is a product that hardens nails. My daughter Lynn, who's always had trouble with her nails, has been using it, and she now has the most beautiful nails I've ever seen.

JEAN: All right! I'm going to try it, and maybe before we're finished with this book, I'll have a different story to tell.

(Note by Jean: I paid $3.50 for a bottle of nail hardener and used it faithfully twice a week, according to directions, for about three weeks. At the end of the third week all ten finger nails broke off at the quick. I telephoned the manufacturer of the product—one of the most reliable cosmetic companies in the country—and reported what had happened. The company gave me my money back and told me that I must be allergic to the product. At this point I have no happy ending to report.)

JEAN: I love the way you do your eyes, Virginia. I'm sure they're very expressive eyes to start with, but what are your makeup procedures?

VIRGINIA: Eye makeup is one of the great things that has come out of the last ten years. The eyes are the most beautiful part of the face, and I thoroughly approve of the concentration on eye makeup. I think eyebrows are terribly important. An ample amount of hair over the eye does something to soften all the features. My eyebrows originally made those of John L. Lewis look plucked. They were thick, straight, bushy brown brows that grew directly across like two highways that almost met. I have had to have them plucked to quite a thin line, and then with a brown pencil I have created an arch where there was no

24

arch before. I make tiny strokes with the pencil, powder as I go along to blend in the line, and then I brush out the brows with a little brush. You can buy a special brush for your brows or use an old mascara brush that has been thoroughly washed.

The upper part of my eyelid just below the brow is quite full. With a little bit of brown shadow I have learned to take away what would otherwise be a lumpy look. By trial and error over a long period of time I have learned that a light-brown shadow is best for me and for my brown eyes. I've tried turquoise and green and lavender, but I always go back to the light brown. It works best for me.

The professionals tell you to use a dark-brown rather than a black eyeliner for a softer look. I've faithfully tried the brown, but it makes my skin look drained. Black enhances my skin tones. That's why I use it. For a lasting effect, I prefer a liquid eyeliner which I apply in one quick stroke just above the lashes on the upper lid. I also use a tiny bit on the lower lid, very gently, just enough to give the lower lashes definition. I use black mascara. At first I wore false eyelashes only on camera. But they do such marvelous things for my eyes that I now put them on almost as automatically as lipstick.

To minimize the dark areas under my eyes I use a lightener, which I apply with my fingertips. I don't powder over the lightened area. I use paste rouge high on my cheeks. By applying it high and far out on the cheekbones, I give myself color and at the same time make my face look thinner.

My lips are very dry. I find that wearing lipstick all the time eases the dryness. The very pale shades are not for me. I love full-bodied reds with peach or rose tones depending on the clothes I am wearing. My lipsticks are not dark, but neither are they washed out. They have clear, definite color. I apply a white base to my lips first, then my lipstick, smoothing it on directly from the stick. I blot and reapply. Then, using either a lipstick brush or my finger, I rub a little bit of gloss on the lower lip. The highlighting gloss works its way to the upper lip, but I do not apply it directly there in order to avoid feathering of the color into the tiny skin creases along the upper lip.

I believe in powder. A few incredibly gorgeous girls can get away with the unpowdered look, but I can't, and I wager you can't, either. I use a cake powder in a misty rose tone which I puff on generously. My favorite evening compact requires loose powder. Do you know what I do? With a nail file I break up a bit of the cake powder and put it in my compact.

I've told you before that I've been using the same cream since I was eighteen years old. It was fabulous then, and it is still fine for me. Apparently it meets my skin needs perfectly for cleansing and lubrication. And happily it is very inexpensive.

That's my whole makeup story. Now I'm a little sorry I told you because I don't want you copying me. Your needs are different. But I do want you to realize that there is nothing mysterious or terribly complicated about makeup. When I heard an anthropologist state recently that men and women wore makeup before they wore clothes, I really wasn't surprised. If you had to make a choice between skin paint and clothes, which would you choose? The next time conversation ebbs around the dinner table, toss out that tricky question—and duck.

4

Your Husband
and the New You

A friend from Iowa was visiting me recently, and I can only say that she is absolutely a pattern for a bridge table because she is square. All she needs are four legs and a deck of cards and you could start to play. She told me that every night she dresses up in her baby doll pajamas, and you know, the image of this woman in baby dolls gave me insomnia for three nights. Her husband is either blind or goes to bed early. He's getting thinner and thinner and no one knows why. But if she looked at herself in the mirror she'd know she killed his appetite. It's so ridiculous for women to think that the clothes they wear, even if their figures are enchanting, will make them look young. They're going about looking their best in the wrong way.

I know many people might say to me, "Look, there's a lot about you I don't like." Maybe they don't like the fact that I discovered false eyelashes years ago and adore them. They may think my hair is too blond. But frankly I am not terribly concerned about what other people think. I'm concerned about the fact that with this color hair, with the eyelashes, and with the other things I do, I function at my best. I have found a personal image that is acceptable and helps me perform to the best of my ability.

JEAN: The missing link is how you relate what is out there in the stores, in the magazines, and on the models, to yourself.

VIRGINIA: Do you think there should be a course given to help evaluate yourself? Someone may say, "Madam, your bosom is the biggest part of you, so we must help you minimize it." Or, "Your eyes are too close together so we have to re-arch the brows and give you a shading of makeup to . . ." Aren't you then just taking the opinion of one person?

JEAN: Well, at some point you're going to have to turn to an authority. Who will it be?

VIRGINIA: One thing I know: It isn't your husband, or your family, or your circle of friends, who are so used to you in a certain way that even if you look a hundred percent better in a new hair style or new makeup, they won't accept it. I remember, when I worked at Mitchell Field as a driver during the war, that the boys who were coming home hadn't seen their wives in two or three years. We talked to the young wives and tried to find out what they were wearing, how their hair was done, and what perfume they used, when they last saw their husbands. We thought it important for the husband, when he got off the plane, to find the woman he left. Some men get a tremendous consolation in what is familiar and known to them. And of course many men find comfort in the wife who ages with them.

On the other hand, when a woman who is gray and drab-looking says to me, "My husband loves me this way," I wonder whether he feels that if he keeps her plain enough she won't listen to the flattery of other men, or whether she reminds him of his mother. We can't be every woman's analyst, or every man's. But one thing I do believe—every woman should dress for herself.

JEAN: But you've assumed, then, that she has a good sense of style and a clear image of herself. I think the big problem is that so many women don't really know who they are. They don't go so far as to consciously imitate Marlene Dietrich or Julie Christie, or whoever is in the headlines that week. But they're not quite sure what their own individual image is, so they jump from one thing to another, from one type of clothes or makeup to another.

VIRGINIA: What makes them unsure? Do you think it's the young daughter who ridicules her mother? Or the husband who says, "Take it off. I won't go out with you if you wear it."? Then she goes to a party and everyone else is wearing exactly what he made her take off. This insistence of the husband that it's okay for other women but not for his wife is an important giveaway of the male insecurity that is dominating the woman's wardrobe.

JEAN: But what bothers me is, How do you give this woman courage to dress for herself or make her own decision in the face of her husband's disapproval? Suppose she finds something she feels marvelous in but knows it will be greeted with contempt at home. What does she do?

VIRGINIA: That's just it. If women had this basic courage, books like this wouldn't have to be written.

JEAN: On the other hand, women can be loaded with basic courage and go out and make monkeys of themselves. A quiet housewife may have a suppressed desire to look like Auntie Mame, and if we tell her to use her own judgment, what happens when she arrives at the PTA in an ostrich-trimmed jumpsuit?

VIRGINIA: I think we have to go back to the mirror—that most fantastic of inventions. I think you can tell about a woman's basic adjustment to herself by the size of the mirrors in her bedroom. The woman who has a dresser mirror that shows only the best part of her and does not have a full-length mirror, is an escapist who can sit with a box of candy and a fudge sundae and have a ball. Then there is the type who has the dressing table mirror with the electric light bulbs that absolutely make you look like you're having a living autopsy. I haven't arrived quite at that stage. I have always been an above-the-waist mirror looker-into until recently, when we had long mirrors put on the doors throughout our apartment. It was not done for my clothes, but for the back of my hair. I think that was when I went on a diet—the day the long mirrors were installed.

But I'm talking about the woman who tries on a dress in a store, looks at herself and says, "I never looked like that before. What's wrong with your mirror?"

Now what if you look at yourself with all honesty and see someone who is not much—your impulse is to turn the mirror's face to the wall. What can you do then? I think the first thing is to want so badly and desperately to change yourself that nothing will stop you. I met a very handsome woman recently

30

who had been the most incredible ugly duckling in her early years. When a friend of mine who hadn't seen her for years heard me say how good-looking she is, the friend exclaimed: "That woman good-looking? Impossible! Nobody could be good-looking with her jaw line and her nose and her terrible skin." Yet this woman with the bad jaw line and the bad nose and the bad skin with patience and time made herself good-looking because she wanted to. She studied herself and decided at what weight the contours of her face were most becoming. She looked at women and she studied them. She accepted what was useful to her and rejected the rest. She tried her hair long and short and a dozen different ways and finally decided on long hair with a center part, the hair pulled softly across the cheeks to a low chignon in back.

Now suppose you invest time and effort in designing a new image for yourself. You get home and your husband takes one look and screams, "Was the other person hurt? I see you've been in a head-on collision." Men are so unbelievably retarded about accepting beauty advances in women. The worst of it is that the same style they loathe in you catches their eye in another woman, and they say, "Doesn't she look stunning."

Men hate any change. This is part of the old Adam technique. Adam, who became one of the greatest fruit lovers in the world, refused his first apple. So when you have a totally new hair style in an entirely new color, the minute you come in, say to him: "How marvelous you look. That's my favorite tie." Or attack him with, "Oh, you're so handsome. One of my friends was saying to me, 'You must have to work hard to keep yourself attractive for John.'"

Use your own words, but build him up. Don't give him a chance to say anything. And don't, by any stretch of foolishness, shove your new head at him and demand, "How do you

31

like it?" If he hasn't said a word, it's not that he hasn't noticed. He's noticed, all right, but maybe not in terms of the details of what you've done. I've known women to go three shades lighter without having their husbands become aware that peroxide had entered their relationship. But he has noticed that you look fine, and that's all right with him.

One tip—if you're making a big change in your hair style, go easy on the spray the first time around. If you give him skin abrasions from the spray he'll dislike the whole thing. One woman tells me that the only way her husband knows she loves him is that she lets him kiss her the night she comes home from the beauty parlor. You gain nothing at all if your hair style makes you unapproachable.

People always ask me how Harry likes my hair styles. People always want to know the oddest things about Harry, and they make the oddest comments. A beautician I know, who saw his picture in my autobiography, said to me, "I had no idea Harry was so good-looking. He's just gorgeous. Weren't you lucky!" Of course that remark made me feel like the loser of the week, but at least she was happy about Harry's looks. Well, every time I've changed my hair style, Harry has said, "This I like." Seems he didn't like the one I just had, although he'd admired it at the time. "You've found something that looks good," he'd add. "Keep it." If I changed my hair again the next week, he'd say, "This is it. Leave it this way."

Well, I can't help it if Harry's reaction to change is the opposite of most men's. My advice to other women is to sneak the change in gradually over a period of weeks so that his eye slowly becomes accustomed to your new look. Or if you want to do it all at once, make it up to him with the sweetness of your attitude toward him, and you might arrange with someone whose opinion he truly respects to exclaim in his hearing: "That's a great new way to wear your hair, Sue. I hope Ken has the sense to like it." If he growls, "I hate it"—well, I suppose you had your reasons for marrying him.

Some of the richest men in the world, I've noticed from reading the papers—and I guess you have, too—have, after many years, abandoned their wives. Each time I've been frantic to see the picture of the woman they remarry. In most cases they remarry the same wife, only younger. Same face—only younger. But I will tell you this, some of these new wives have been very plain, very natural-looking; some almost too much so for my taste. One new wife I recall, who was close to forty, had long hair down her back, like a teen-ager. It may be a studied casualness, but I am suspicious of a certain kind of studied casualness. It looks to the outside world as if it was achieved merely with a toss of the head. But in reality, hours and hours of time were spent before the mirror to achieve that particular thrown-together look. I wonder how the men feel when they discover that their new nature girl is really a highly contrived creature.

And that brings to my mind the question: How boring is the subject of personal beauty to a man?

JEAN: I think it's the quickest way on earth to bore a man. He doesn't want to hear about the mechanics of beauty and he doesn't want it to interfere with his life in any way.

VIRGINIA: In any warm personal relationship between a husband and a wife, or between a mother and a child who seeks the comfort of snuggling up to her, a coiffure or makeup should never prevent her from giving the love that those close to her deserve. I know that the minute I get into the taxi to visit my own grandchild, I take out a tissue and off comes my lipstick. I cannot wait for that baby to put her arms out to give me a hug.

And I don't want to push her away because she might ruin my hair or smear my lipstick. I'd rather have my hair a little disheveled than greet that loving, spontaneous child with a "Now, don't touch." It's the same thing in your relationship with your husband or beau. There are times, of course, when you've dressed and made up to the teeth. Why does he always want to kiss you then? Because you look your best, that's why. He's telling you something. Get the message.

This approachability is also a part of naturalness. For example, when do you set your hair? To what lengths do you go to conceal from your husband the fact that you make a genuine effort to look the way you do? Harry and I have been married for thirty years. I can't think of a night after our wedding when I didn't use bobby pins. When we lived in the suburbs I'd start setting my hair in the car while we were driving home at night, to save time. One of the Gabor girls once told me that she puts curlers in when she steps into a hot tub, and her hair is all ready when she gets out. Well, mine would look like the hot tub. Not many people have hair that bounces up. Mine needs eight or ten hours of tender encouragement. And even then it needs a lot of special handling.

I only wish I could talk to husbands for a moment about exercising their heart muscles by telling their wives that they approve of them. All of this effort the wives are making is for a little applause, and applause comes in many ways—from a look in a man's eyes, from an extra kiss or pat of approval. It's so easy for a man to applaud his wife for her efforts; and if you are really truthful with yourself, look at your husband some time when he's looking at you, and if you see an expression that you don't like, you'd better take a look at yourself.

5

Time Doesn't Tell

So many women seem to have the mistaken idea that beauty is confined to the very young. Recently Joan Crawford was on "Girl Talk," and I don't ever remember her being as beautiful as she is now. In fact, when I look at some of her old movies at night on TV, I just marvel that she is now so much more beautiful and poised than she was then. Today she is in her mid-fifties and lovely. Her figure is slim but not too slim. I, for one, do not find beauty in a too thin woman after a certain age. The dehydrated look is a dried-up, aging look, and I think the woman past her middle

35

years who overdiets and overdenies herself takes on a dehydrated personality.

Joan Crawford in her middle years is a far more glamorous and vibrant personality than she was as a young star. Her beautifully cared-for looks, her enormous interest in the fast-changing world around her, her entirely contemporary viewpoint, give her a beauty that is truly matchless.

That's why I want you to look in the mirror and see what you honestly are. Don't blame the mirror if you don't look like Audrey Hepburn, or if you look old enough to be Twiggy's grandmother. Don't allow the mirror to throw you. Accept what you see and try to do the best with it. I do believe that a woman's naturalness and serenity—provided she is not quiet because she's dying inside—are what give her beauty.

Then, of course, I have to go back to the foliage. When people send you rosebuds it is with the hope that you will have long enjoyment because the flowers are at their best days later, when they bloom. If we look at the shrubbery, it is in the fall of the year, just before the long twilight of winter when it becomes gray and drab, that the foliage turns autumnally inspiring —gold and bronze and red. This is why I feel that color is so important to every woman, especially in her maturing years.

Drabness is not a chronological thing. I have found many young people very drab. My father once told me that there are a few intangibles that get better as you go along—charm, wisdom, poise, intelligence, understanding, sympathy. These are the qualities that grow with the passing of time.

When you enter a room full of people your eye is automatically drawn to the face that stands out. Now this can be either a grotesquerie or a thing of beauty. Among my friends, the women I find the greatest beauties are those other people often don't think of as attractive when they first meet them. The color, beauty, and vitality of youth has to develop into something else. What I've discovered and what I believe will give my readers hope is that among the young suburban women today thirty is their most difficult age hurdle. The young women seem to be classifying themselves as geriatric cases. This may be because there is an airline that retires its stewardesses at thirty-two—which to me is barely post-kindergarten. Our whole tempo of life has made women age-conscious. But remember this: the one thing that will age you more than anything else is being age-conscious.

Natural beauties so often fade the fastest. Many girls who start out with a great natural bloom, who are always told how marvelous they look, take their appearance for granted, don't make any effort, don't acquire good beauty habits. Quite often by thirty-five they're outdistanced by the earlier ugly ducklings who did not get the compliments when they were young but who, now in maturity, develop a style and a dash and a confidence that will always be with them. Nothing is sadder than the remnants of beauty. I'm not talking about the ravages of time, because that's something we all face. I speak of the beauty ruined by carelessness or poverty or liquor or great unhappiness, so that when we look at such a woman we say with a sigh, "Imagine how beautiful she must have been once." If she was really once so beautiful, she should still have good bone structure, or wonderful eyes. But neglect and abuse can destroy even the most exceptional natural assets.

Excessive drinking is probably the worst disfigurer of a woman. It removes buoyancy from her skin, which becomes water-logged and discolored. It dulls her eyes. It makes her sag. There is a whole special look to a woman who drinks to excess.

Don't Blame the Mirror

I suppose she has a problem that made her turn to drink in the first place, but her very choice of liquor as an escape clarifies for the world the fact that she has a problem.

Maturity can be one of the greatest advantages in the world. I can't stand women who hide behind the philosophy that they're too old to get work or to make friends. They were too old at twenty. They have always been too old. The person who is eager and enthusiastic is ageless. If I were hiring somebody to work for me, I would want an older woman because she would not be tied down with children, with the emotional disturbances of adjusting to a young marriage, with the illnesses of babies that might keep her home. I would want someone separated by time from these all-consuming energy outlets. And I would welcome her maturity. But I would want her to be dressed neatly and well. I'd like to see makeup on her face, her hair properly groomed, her personality as current as her face.

I think a husband has a right to the same expectations as a prospective employer. I recall a great cosmetics ad: "He'll feel younger just looking at you." When a man marries his contemporary and she allows herself to age unduly, he is constantly reminded of the passage of time by looking at her. But if she's young—not in the sense of being kittenish—and if she has resilience and youthfulness about her, he'll say, "Well, boy, I'm not so old at that."

I have always been honest about my age. I have felt that if people want to know it badly enough they're going to look it up. If you falsify your age, you have to falsify your whole life. You have to give up some of your best memories and best stories, for they reveal you were past the jump-rope stage on VE day, or ancient enough to recall the Charleston, first time around. When I meet a woman, I am inclined to make her younger than she is. I don't really hope for the same courtesy to me, but it would be nice.

I've never traded on youth as a passport to success. I've never felt it was anything but a temporary accommodation. Now, at my age, I am for the first time in my life without competition from other women. I am frankly a mother, frankly a grand-mother. I have guests on my show who are so much more beautiful, so much more accomplished, so much younger. But I am not competing against them. I am working with them. I am not worried that they are going to get my job, because the wisdom I have tried to accumulate through the years gives me strength and fortitude.

I have the marvelous comfort of the experience that comes from living. So I don't envy them. And I wish that women would not feel that every young girl is a tremendous threat. Her excitement about living, her vitality, her enthusiasm—these are threats. But her inexperience is a big liability. You must remain enthusiastic about yourself, about your family, about your husband and his interests. You must be enthusiastic about life.

Enthusiasm is the most effective vitamin of all. There is no plant living that doesn't thrive on it. I think I could close down the old-age homes if only I could pump into them a sufficient supply of enthusiasm. Don't tell me you're tired and have nothing to be enthusiastic about. Because you know what I'll tell you? I'll tell you to leave the dishes in the sink, call up your daughter and tell her you simply can't sit for your grandchild this afternoon—something terribly important has come up. Then, go to your beauty parlor, have the gray in your hair covered, or have your hair tinted a shade or two lighter. Ask the beautician to give you a makeup, very soft and shimmery. (Watch like a hawk the way she does it so you can duplicate

39

her techniques tomorrow.) Then make your husband take you out to dinner, or cook for him something you haven't bothered to prepare for the last dozen years.

Of course you feel younger. And the miracle is catching, for your husband does, too.

6

The ABC's of Makeup

Now let's plunge right in to the colorful but often bewildering world of makeup. I don't blame you for being bewildered if you've glanced at the thousands of items on sale at the beauty counters of your department store, read the magazine ads month after month for new colors, new products, new methods of application, watched endless commercials for new sprays, foundations, lipsticks—each one a whole new breakthrough that will bring you undreamed of beauty and romance. When I survey the counters of a major store, I often begin to believe that there is a different cream for every pore on my face.

"How can I ever master all that?" you demand. "I just get the hang of stick eyeshadow when they tell me I have to use powdered shadow. Should I give up rouge for a blusher? How many brushes do I really need?"

Your trouble is that you're looking at the entire scene backward. That's why you're confused by the overpowering output of the cosmetics companies. Swing yourself around so that you turn your back to the baffling array of products and look at yourself in the mirror. That image, which you probably don't care too much for at the moment, is your face, and it only offers four areas of concern to you and the makeup industry. First, there is the skin itself—your complexion. Second, there are your eyes. Third, there are your lips. Fourth, there's your hair. That's all you are dealing with—skin, eyes, lips, and hair.

Yes, it's true that an energetic manufacturer came out not long ago with a special rouge for ear lobes, but let's just let that pass. Now if we start to consider the products from the point of view of where we put them, we begin to achieve a little order.

Skin: Your complexion is the background for the beauty you are creating. You are involved in no more than three steps in the care of your skin. Your first objective is to keep your skin soft and smooth, to combat dryness, and to delay the aging process. For this you use anywhere from one to a whole trayful of creams and lotions—overnight, under makeup, or both.

Your second goal is to improve the texture and color of your skin by evening out tiny blemishes, lines, and irregularities, by removing shine, and by enhancing contours. You do this with powder alone, with foundation alone, or with a combination of powder and foundation. Foundation may be liquid, cream (in a tube or jar), stick, fluff, or cake that you apply with water or combined with powder. You give color to your cheeks with rouge that comes as stick, cake, cream, or blusher.

Your third job is to remove completely at the end of the day everything you put on your skin. For take-it-off purposes you select from soap, cream, cleansing liquid, and astringent.

Eyes: Until a few years ago, if you owned an eyebrow pencil and some mascara you were as avant-garde as anyone in the eye business. Today, equipment is more elaborate and results are more exciting. Starting at the top and working down, you will need pencils or brush-on coloring for your eyebrows; colored shadow for your lids in the form of stick, cream, cake, or powder; liners for the edge of your lid, applied as pencil or liquid; mascara for your lashes, or, if you want to be completely up to date, lashes for your lashes.

Lips: The requirements here are very simple: lipstick in as many shades as you can afford or find storage room for, and, optionally, a brush for applying lipstick or a lip-outlining pencil, a gloss for highlights.

Hair: The essentials are shampoo, brush, comb, setting materials, and conditioner. You will probably want spray for either regular or occasional use. If you color your hair yourself, you will need a rinse or a tint. You may also give yourself home permanents.

That's it—the whole thing. Now is that so terribly confusing, so impossible to unravel? You'll have to agree it's really astonishingly simple. The trouble sets in when you must decide which type of product in each category is most suitable for you, and which manufacturer's products to choose.

I will not try to influence you on choice of brands, except to say that you may have complete confidence in the purity and integrity of nationally advertised and distributed products. You have a kind of double protection, for not only does the federal government outlaw chemicals and other materials which are injurious, but the large companies, in fiercely competitive spirit, police each other. As soon as a new product hits the market, chemists for competing companies tear it apart to see how it's made and how it works. If their analysis reveals a dye or other ingredient on the forbidden list, there is an immediate complaint to Washington and steps are taken at once. In the early days of the eye makeup craze, a number of New York drug stores carried a line of imported eyeshadow in beautiful gold, silver, and bronze shadings. A chemist for a leading American cosmetics company, seeking to find how the gleaming effects were achieved, discovered that the imported shadows contained metallic substances forbidden by U.S. law to be used near the eye. The offending products disappeared from store counters from one day to the next.

A few pieces of preliminary advice:

1. Read the manufacturer's directions with care. I don't know how to emphasize this point enough. Perhaps if I tell you that some of the companies pay more than $15,000 a year to the woman who writes the copy on boxes and leaflets inside boxes, you will be impressed. This is one of the hardest kinds of prose in the world to write. It must be factual, accurate, and crystal clear. You'd never believe the number of times a simple instruction leaflet is rewritten, edited, and polished to make it foolproof. Yet any number of women throw away these valuable instruction sheets without even glancing at them. Please make it a practice to read from beginning to end the folder in any new product you buy. And it's worth every bit of the time it takes to reread the insert in a familiar package. There may be a new way of applying the product or a new effect you can get by using the product just a little differently.

44

2. Whatever the product is, use it sparingly. About the only exception is cologne or body freshener, which you may want to slather on with a lavish hand on a sultry day. But everything else—foundation, rouge, hair spray, eyeshadow—dole out like a miser. If you don't get enough with the first application, you can always add a little more as you go along. But it is a tiresome and messy business to remove overdone eyeliner or to wipe off excess powder base. You may even in some cases have to wash everything off and start from scratch if you've overpainted your face.

3. Keep all your equipment—brushes, puffs, pads, everything —hospital clean. If you don't remember to have a supply of clean puffs, use little disposable cotton balls. Have sharp points on your makeup pencils. How can you possibly get a fine, delicate line if the pencil is worn down to the width of a blunt crayon?

4. Make up in a good strong light. To avoid shadows on the mirror, arrange, if possible, to have the lights run across the top and along the sides of the mirror, as in a Hollywood dressing room. Avoid a fluorescent light in your bathroom; it changes the color values of lipstick and eye makeup. Use a magnifying glass if you can't see your face clearly in a regular mirror.

5. Practice with brushes and pencils until you achieve a firm, steady line. Eyeliner should go on with a surehanded sweep of the wrist, not with little jiggles of the fingers; little jiggles make smudgy, uneven lines. Practice. Stand in front of the mirror and sweep the pencil right across your eyelid at the very base of the lashes. If the line wavers, take it off and start over. As you get more skill, you will learn to rotate the pencil or brush a bit to get greater width in part of the line so that it has a graceful contour.

7

More ABC's

         All right! Now that we've made some order out of the jungle of beauty products, how do we thread our way through the wilderness to the promised land? What to buy, what to decline, what to laugh at? I can't make the decision for you. I can't balance out your beauty needs, your budget, your psyche. I can only tell you, based on information I have gathered from the leading beauty authorities, what you can expect in performance and benefits from each group of products. After the basic training you get here, I suggest you linger a little longer in the cosmetics section of your department or drug store. Study the new displays. Try out the tester products on your hand. Ask your druggist or his wife or the cosmetician about anything new that intrigues you. He'll have helpful answers because he's been thoroughly briefed by the manufacturer.

If the makeup expert from a large cosmetics company is giving free consultations in your local store, hurry on down. If you don't quite have the courage to offer your own face for a demonstration, join the circle of observers. I recently watched a gifted artist making up a silver-haired woman in a New York store. The woman was pretty but colorless when he started. When he finished, she had the loveliest touch of silver-blue shadow on her eyelids; her gray-white lashes, invisible without mascara, were darkened to make you aware that she had fine blue eyes; her cheeks took on a youthful pink blush, her lips turned soft pink with a gentle, silvery sheen. The spectators burst into spontaneous applause when he finished. I hope she bought every single item he used on her. She was a fool if she didn't.

Background makeup: If your finished face is to be a portrait, your skin is the canvas. Like an artist, you must prepare it. Some skins need only a light dusting of powder. Others require a tinted foundation to improve the complexion color, camouflage tiny blemishes, help hold powder, and keep the skin sheltered with protective moisture during the day.

Cake makeup: This is the favorite of actresses. Applied with a moistened sponge, it gives most complete coverage, can be used to hide a multitude of sins and to change the complexion from a sallow yellow to a warm peach. Many women, however, find this type of makeup drying. Others are not happy with the overall painted look they get, especially if they apply it too lavishly. A spare cake around the house is good for emergency use—when you get out of a sickbed, for example, too wan to face the world in your normal makeup.

Liquid foundation: The makeup that comes in a bottle may contain a great deal of oil, very little oil, or no oil at all. You'll have to ask the salesgirl to explain the content of the brand you select. You would not want a makeup with a great deal of oil if you have oily skin. Neither would you want a non-oily liquid for dry skin. You usually have to shake a liquid foundation and apply it sparingly with your fingertips over every part of your face and down just below the jawline, to blend it into your throat. There should never be a sharp line of demarcation where the makeup ends.

Rich cream foundations also come in tubes and jars. Medicated makeups contain antiseptics and other ingredients to discourage pimples and acne. Pressed powder blended with foundation is packaged in compacts to provide more tint and coverage than powder alone.

Choosing the proper shade of foundation is not always easy. If your skin naturally has a pleasing tone you can select a foundation that is close to your skin color, perhaps a trifle darker. If your skin is too ruddy, a foundation with a good deal of beige will cool it off. A peach or rose foundation will pick up a sallow complexion. Be sure to check your foundation shade in summer when you begin to acquire a tan. Unless you are painting your face like a wall, the final coloring should be a becoming blend of your natural skin tones and the makeup you add.

As a guide to shade selection, Clairol has evolved a fascinating concept. The company's expertise in hair color has led it to recognize the importance of hair color in the choice of foundation, powder, and lipstick. A redhead with a pale ivory skin, for example, requires a different foundation and a different lipstick from a blond or a dark brunette with the same skin tones. You realize the logic of this idea if you have changed your hair color. When you went from brown hair to blond, you found that your makeup required more muted, subtler coloring. You should always be aware of your hair color, especially if it is very light or very dark or very red, when selecting makeup.

Powder: You apply powder generously with a puff, either directly to the skin or over foundation that has been allowed to dry. Powder is usually a trifle darker than the foundation it is worn with. Translucent, no-color powder has come into popularity recently. It gives an ideal, powdered look without adding color. You should puff powder on generously, pressing the puff over the entire face and throat. Then go over the face with a piece of cotton or a soft brush, using downward strokes. Go over eyelashes, eyebrows, and hair edges with an eyebrow brush, to even off the makeup.

Rouge: You use rouge for a healthy glow and to deepen the color of the eyes. Never, never in little clown circles, please. Rouge should be applied outward from the cheekbone and blended in carefully. Dry rouge, applied with puff or cotton after powdering, is the easiest to apply. Dust with more powder to soften the edges. Cream rouge, applied with fingertip before the foundation is completely dry and before powdering, is longer lasting. Liquid rouge, longest lasting of all, must be blended in very quickly while the foundation is still moist.

Blush: This is a new makeup that has swept the country simply because it does so much for the face with so little effort. It comes in a cake in a range of shades and is flicked on with a thick artist's brush. The original use was for the cheeks, to impart an instant blush of color. Many women use it all over—very, very gently—for a glow that makes them look just back from vacation. Girls with jobs have told me that a fast once-over with blush and a quick touch of mascara and eye shadow will get them from the office to a cocktail date in one minute flat.

Contouring: You hear more and more these days about using foundation or powder to contour the face. This is an old trick of stage makeup, and the makeup artists for "Girl Talk" are great experts at it. The optical principle is very simple. What is light comes forward toward you; what is dark, recedes. By using two shades of foundation it is possible to reshape the face. For example, if your forehead is too big and broad, try using foundation and powder one or two shades darker above your eyes. If your face is too broad at the cheeks, use a darker foundation from the cheekbones outward. If your jaw is too wide, try the darker color along the jawline. A touch of darker foundation at the tip of an overlong nose will tend to shorten it. If your chin is too tiny, a lighter foundation will bring it into better focus. Or if your face is too narrow at the jaw, lighter makeup in that area will give an illusion of width.

This isn't plastic surgery, so don't expect miracles. You'll have to practice to keep from looking striped or simply smeared. If your regular foundation is very light textured and nearly translucent, you may have to use a heavier foundation or even a cake makeup to get proper contouring results. Some day when you're terribly depressed, try reshaping your face with makeup. You might invent a whole new face for yourself.

Eyes: Your objective as far as your eyes are concerned is to make them beautiful and expressive. Eyebrows should be plucked from beneath until they are neat and gently arched. I like strong brows; there are beauty experts who don't. You will probably have to perfect the line with a pencil which you must keep very sharp and use in short, tiny strokes—never in a heavy line. Don't use a black pencil unless you have coal black hair. You might get a more natural look if you combine a light and a dark brown pencil. Try light brown and gold if you are a blond. The newest eyebrow color comes in a cake and is brushed on. It is subtler than a pencil, a luxury touch.

Eyeshadow: This is used on the surface of the eyelid for coloring and contouring. A few years ago most women used shadow in blue, green, turquoise, or violet to match either the color of their eyes or the color of their dresses. The tendency was to apply colored shadow on the outer half of the lid and upward toward the brow. Today shadow is usually more neutral and more natural. A soft pastel shadow, applied sparingly and gently, is still acceptable. A definite swath of strong color is out—except for spectacular evening effects. White has come into enormous favor as a shadow. It is used directly over the lids and under the brow, provided the bone structure is pretty and not too prominent. If the bone sticks out or there is puffiness in the lids, a beige or pale brown shadow is recommended.

Cream shadow, which comes in little pots or in sticks, rather like lipstick, is often the most satisfactory form for the woman who has crepey or lined lids. The cream is easy to apply and its lubricating effect is beneficial. Shadow also comes as powder pressed into little cakes and is applied either with a brush or with your fingertip. While the coloring of powdered eyeshadow is extremely delicate on the eye, its lasting power is not so great. Shadow is also available in little paintboxes, like a child's water colors, to be applied with a brush or sponge dampened in water. The cake shadow permits great precision of design and feathering of one color into another.

Eyeliner: The accent line applied to the eyelids along the base of the lashes is called eyeliner. In the first flowering of eye makeup a few years back, many women became devoted to strong, even garish liner colors. Today a fiercely blue or green line, even if it precisely matches a scarf or dress, looks dated. The tendency now is to view the eyeliner as a technique for defining the eyes and enhancing the lashes. That is why most experts today choose a black or dark-brown liner. It should begin as the merest thread at the inner corners and build up a bit toward the center and the outer corners. The little lift at the outer corners is optional. Above the black or dark-brown liner at the outer part of the eye, many women apply a second line in a soft pastel color to echo the color of their eyes. The broad mourning band of black on the lids, adored by many models, is not for the average woman.

Liquid liner applied with a brush gives the most sharply defined accent, but must be used as sparingly as possible. Many women use a special liner pencil which has an extra fine point, or they rely on their eyebrow pencil. A pencil will glide on more smoothly if you first apply foundation or a touch of cream to the lids. Many actresses use black pancake makeup as eyeliner. An eyeshadow stick can also be used effectively as a liner, but avoid heavy strokes of color. When applying liner, do not pull the lid at the corner and stretch it. You will get a jagged line. You can stop your eye from blinking by pressing your finger lightly against the bone at the outer corner of the eye, without tugging on the lid.

Mascara: The coloring is applied to the lashes themselves. Black and dark brown are the most popular colors. The mascara wand has largely replaced cake or cream mascara, which was applied with a brush. Many experts recommend using mascara on both the upper and lower surfaces of the upper lashes. If the lashes stick together you can separate them with a dry brush.

The lashes on the lower lid are an open question. If you use liner, mascara, or both there, you need a touch as fragile as swans-down. Any heavy accent on the lower lid, unless you are a very young, doe-eyed, ballerina type who can get away with almost anything, turns into a caricature. On the other hand, the merest trace of liner on the lower lid often makes the eye appear larger. And a faint brushing of mascara gives the lower lashes a pretty fringed look. However, too much mascara on the lower lashes will cast an undesirable shadow under the eyes.

Lash Lengtheners: Bits of lintlike material are embedded in mascara or applied separately to the lashes with a brush. The mascara causes the tiny particles to adhere to the lashes, making them both longer and thicker.

Lips: Lipstick is probably your single most important make-up item—the one you would least like to be caught on a desert island without. Textures vary from fairly dry-feeling on the lips to very, very creamy moist. The choice is up to you. Many lipsticks today are blended with protective ingredients that reduce chapping. Choice of color depends on the hue of your skin, the color of your hair, and the color of your costume. The blending of lipstick with costume is especially important if you are wearing a dress or blouse anywhere in the red family. A pink-purple lipstick with a clear red dress is a disaster. A bright red lipstick can ruin the effect of a coral outfit.

If you are past thirty you probably won't look your best with a very pale, whitened lipstick. Under incandescent lights peach and orange tones tend to wash out. That's why what the trade calls a blue lipstick is recommended for evening. A blue lipstick is really red, but with deep pink or raspberry tones predominating. I apply my lipstick directly from the stick and get a sharp, even outline every time. But the recommended method is with a lipstick brush. The Toilet Goods Association suggests the following technique:

> Rub the brush on the lipstick, taking up sufficient to trace a smooth, clean line around the lips. Have lips relaxed, with mouth closed. Do upper lip first, starting at the right-hand corner and working to the center. Reverse brush and do left side. To do the lower lip, draw a straight line across the center. Then from the corner, draw a full rounded curve down to meet this line. Repeat entire operation with lips slightly apart and smiling. Powder lips lightly and blot with tissue. Then fill in with lipstick. Let set a couple of minutes and blot with tissue. If shinier lips are desired repeat use of lipstick and blot lightly.

The new lip glosses are also excellent for giving a shimmer to lipstick. If you don't like the shape of your lips you can draw an outline with a lipstick brush either beyond or within your normal lip line. If you are making your lips smaller, be sure to apply foundation first over your mouth to blot out the lip line. If your underlip is too heavy, use a slightly darker shade of lipstick on it to make it recede. If your lips are too thin you can build up a fuller shape with a darker lipstick, then apply a lighter shade on top, not extending it all the way to the new edge you have created.

Skin care: Your first obligation is total cleansing, every day, not just sometimes. I am not going to tell you whether to use a soap or a cleanser. If you've been a soap girl all your life, you might enjoy giving some of the creamy new cleansers a whirl. Not at all greasy, they are extremely effective.

Unless the jar or bottle states otherwise, you should spread cleansing cream on your neck, chin, cheeks, nose, and forehead. With more cream on your fingertips, massage with both hands your neck—both back and front—with upward strokes. With still more cream massage from center chin to ears. Raise fingers and massage from cheeks to temples, under eyes and over eyelids. Massage cleansing cream down nose and across upper lip. Apply cream upward and outward to the hairline on the forehead to protect the brow from frown lines.

Wrap tissues around your hands to remove the cream, using the same motions as when applying. Finish the cleansing with a toner applied with cotton. If your skin is oily you can tolerate a fairly brisk astringent. If it is dry you will prefer a milder freshener.

Should you go to bed with cream on your face? I don't, but maybe you should. There are new creams that are nongreasy. They have oils that lubricate the skin and moisturizing ingredients that restore the moisture balance needed to keep skin soft and youthful looking. If you're fascinated by luxury creams, the sky's the limit. From orchid pollen to placenta extract, from queen bee jelly to mysterious hormones, from turtle oil to peach kernel oil—the choice is yours. Have fun if you wish.

Masks and grains: These are great for an at-home facial. The preparations tighten on the skin as they dry and then are peeled off a few minutes later. They firm the pores, draw off impurities, stimulate circulation. Try them for a big event or when you are feeling low.

Under makeup: Many women use a moisture cream or lotion under makeup for added protection against drying. This is often a good idea in winter, not essential in summer. But make sure you need all that extra emollience on your face. One school of beauty experts feels that what many women believe is dry skin is really excessively oily or overoiled skin. The overdose of oil packs down the tiny particles of skin that normally flake off during cleansing and they form a scaly coating that is mistaken for a dried-out skin surface. If you suspect this might be your problem, cut back on the amount of cream you use and try a more intensive cleansing.

Hand creams: Use them generously on hands, elbows, feet. Use after each washing with a putting-on-the-glove motion. Massage down each finger, pushing back the cuticle as you massage. If your hands are absolutely dried out, try cotton gloves over creamed hands for a few nights (if your husband is away), or during the day around the house. If your hands get badly soiled from house or office work, use cream before washing. Creams with silicone can be used before heavy work to prevent penetration by dirt and grease.

Body preparations: If you can't bring yourself to buy them, hint about the body lotions, aerosols, and satiners for Christmas or birthdays. Most of them are perfumed and sheer heaven for making you feel pampered and loved.

Sun products: The sun is your deadly enemy unless you meet it on the proper terms. It can age and wither your skin faster than illness. Dermatologists are unanimously opposed to unlimited sun bathing. Your skin becomes toughened, leathery, dehydrated. Chronically overbaked skin seems to become more susceptible to cancer. Sun-screening creams, lotions, and aerosols have chemical ingredients that block out damaging rays. Moisturizing elements reduce drying. Keep your suntan lotion within arm's length at the beach or pool or aboard a boat, and reapply frequently.

Hand care: There is no excuse for raggedy nails and cuticles. I'm not going to list all the nail polish and cuticle-care preparations—they are inexpensive, simple to use, and a small bottle lasts almost forever. If you don't have a professional manicure periodically, you must give yourself half an hour each week to catch up with your nails. I don't see how you can resist the new polishes—they're so pearly and beautiful.

JEAN: Virginia, remember some time back you were scolding me about my unpolished nails? Well, I've made the most wonderful discovery in the world. I bought a set of false fingernails at my drugstore. They were made in England; each nail is a gorgeous oval, permanently polished in the palest of pale iridescent pink. I had to file each nail down at the base to fit my fingers. It took about twenty minutes to get them the right shape. A special adhesive comes in the package, and another container of adhesive remover. The first time it took me about fifteen minutes to get the nails on. Now I can whisk them on in about a minute. They are so beautiful I can't believe it. At first I was unaccustomed to the extra length of my nails and awkward; I found it hard to handle things. Now I even wear them when I type. I wear them for about three days at a time, take them off, slip them back into their box, and they're always ready to slide back on my fingers when I want to look elegant and ladylike.

VIRGINIA: I'm glad you discovered the nails. Now I don't have to be sorry you've brought your hands along when you come to see me.

I think by now I've covered the major output of the cosmetician's art. The choice should be less bewildering for you. If you know the products, know your skin, know your needs, you can have fun with makeup. Let yourself go for an evening gala—brush glitter over all your face, scatter brilliants in your hair, let your eyelids shimmer. You'll have a marvelous time! And if you want to scare the daylights out of your friends and family, take a tip from a way-out film on makeup screened recently for the New York Fashion Group, an organization of the city's leading fashion insiders. The makeup artist painted beautiful blue eyes on the eyelids of a model dressed in a bikini. The canny girl could sleep on the beach with her eyes wide open, never missing a trick.

8

Do Your Eyes Have It?

PROBLEM: I can't tame my false eyelashes.

The care and application of false lashes can be very baffling to a beginner. Those two little hairy strips seem to lead a life of their own and leap about like mercury. Makeup expert Evelyn Marshall, who has pioneered in bringing tricks and products of professional models and actresses to the average woman, is able to apply her lashes in two minutes flat without a mirror in a dark telephone booth. This is her advice:

New lashes must be cut down to the proper length. They

should extend from the outer corner of your eyelid to one-quarter of an inch away from the inner corner. Cut your new lashes to this length with scissors. Many women hate to throw away that little bit of lash they've paid for. But the quarter to half inch discarded may be the difference between success and failure. Most lashes today come already feathered—that is, they have a jagged effect along the edges the way eyelashes grow naturally. If your false lashes are straight-edged like a comb, snip them irregularly with manicure scissors to give them a more natural look. The lashes should be a little bit shorter at the inner end.

Now take a lash and hold it upside down between thumb and forefinger of your left hand (if you are right-handed), with the cord to which the individual lashes are attached exposed. Run the tube of adhesive along the cord, squeezing out a tiny bit across the entire length. Now take the lash at its outer end with a pair of tweezers and sit it against the outside corner of your eye, applying the cord of the lash against the very edge of the lid where your own eyelashes grow. The false lash should be applied right next to the roots of your own lashes, not to the surface of the eyelid where normally you place eyeliner.

Using the edge of an emery board, press the lash cord into position on your eyelid. Always start positioning the lid from the outer corner. Never shut your eyes while applying. On new lashes you may apply eyeliner along the cord of the lash strip and at the very edge of your eyelid. Using an eyebrow brush or a mascara brush, brush real and false lashes together. Use a small amount of mascara if you wish.

Hard to do? Not at all if you'll take a few dry runs at your dressing table mirror. A word from the experienced: Never apply lashes when you're in a frantic hurry, the children are screaming, and your husband is tapping his foot with impatience. You'll get the jitters, do everything backward, and arrive at the party with your lashes askew and your poise shattered.

PROBLEM: I wear glasses. How do I make the most of my makeup?

First you have to select frames in the most flattering shape and color. Try on many shapes and varieties. View yourself in a full-length mirror to make sure the frame is in proper proportion to your build and your face. In the past, lighter tone frames were recommended for pale or pink-toned complexions; deeper tones for those with darker complexions. More recently women have favored dark-framed glasses that definitely assert their presence. If you have a limited wardrobe of glasses, keep them simple. If you can afford a wide variety, then you can have gingham frames to match your sport clothes.

Makeup experts at the Helena Rubinstein salon tell women to stop hiding behind their glasses. Since the glasses are there for all to see, they must be accepted and incorporated into the makeup scheme. Lenses that magnify will intensify the color and effect of eye makeup. Liner, shadow, and mascara behind such glasses must always be in soft, muted colors. A sharp blue or green shadow will appear garish through these lenses. Behind nonmagnifying and tinted lenses, colors are diminished. You may have to use a more clearly defined color to get a pleasing effect. Experiment both with and without glasses in a strong light.

Don't let your eyebrows conflict with the top of your frames or disappear behind them. You may have to heighten the brow-line slightly. Be sure it is kept very tidy. You apply

61

foundation and face powder with your glasses off and dust away excess powder around your eyes so that it doesn't gather in crease lines. Rouge goes on the cheekbone below the eyeglass area. Avoid a pursed, rosebud mouth. Lips with wider, gentler curves give a better balance with glasses.

If you can't see to apply eye makeup with your glasses off and don't have room to maneuver your brushes with glasses on, here's a helpful tip. Place a mirror, either plain or magnifying, flat on a table in a good, strong light. Now look down to apply your eye makeup. You will find it easy to look at yourself in the mirror either through or over your glasses, and you will be able to reach over the top of your glasses to apply liner, shadow, and mascara. You will need practice to acquire dexterity in this unfamiliar position, but the results will be worth the effort.

PROBLEM: I have circles under my eyes.

Dark circles or shadows under the eyes can be made less noticeable by the use of a special cover cream which comes in light flesh tints and is available in a tube, like lipstick, or as a cream to be applied with fingertips. Another way to camouflage circles is with a foundation a few shades lighter than that used for the rest of your face. You can also paint out the dark areas with white lipstick or white eyeshadow. Powder over the merest fleck of powder to reduce sheen but avoid caking.

PROBLEM: My eyes are too small and too close together.

The expert we called on to help solve this problem is Pablo, Elizabeth Arden's famed face designer. For the fashion magazines he creates eyes as brilliant and imaginative as butterfly wings. For the average woman he opens up the small, unobtrusive eye to beauty it never had before. Says Pablo: "Every woman's face looks better when her eyes are beautifully made up." The Pablo eye for daytime is made up with utmost subtlety. Pablo begins by minimizing the eyebrow. He shapes it to a graceful arch, thins it if necessary, colors it only with the faintest, most delicate brush strokes, using cake eyeliner. It is his revolutionary view that a strong, decisive eyebrow detracts from the eye itself. His brows are intentionally de-emphasized.

Working with colors that come in cake form and fine-pointed brushes that he dips in water, Pablo goes to work on the eyelid. He draws an extremely thin line in black or dark brown as close as possible to the lashes, moving his brush from the inner to the outer corner of the eye. The line widens slightly toward the center and outer corner of the eye and ends just a tiny fraction beyond the eye's outer end with a slight lift. Above this line he brushes on a small amount of white shadow. In the crease of the eyelid he shades in a bit of beige or brown shadow to give the eyes a deep-set look and shades it to white again under the brow. He applies a tiny dot of white shadow at the inner and outer corner of each eye to give a widening effect. He sometimes gently runs a blue pencil just above the lower lashes. In contrast to the blue, the white of the eye looks whiter and therefore the whole eye appears bigger. He applies mascara delicately to both upper and lower lashes. To achieve the best effect, he advises women to look down and coat the upper side of the upper lashes, then look up and cover the lower side.

We suggest you try the Pablo technique on just one eye to test its extraordinary eye-opening effect.

9

Counter-Attack

I am fascinated by the marvelous women who inhabit the world of beauty salesmanship. They operate on the door-to-door level, in your drugstore, in a beauty salon, or in a department store. Very frankly, I find these women exciting. I love to walk by the counters to enjoy the aura of perfume and peach chiffon and the incredible skins these girls have that make alabaster look like cardboard in comparison. I always wonder if when babies are born some fate determines which one shall go out in the world to become a beautician or cosmetologist, because these girls have a certain special look about them—a marvelous, powdered, makeup look.

Since nature does not enhance skin color or texture as we grow older, I rely increasingly on these cosmetologists at beauty counters. I've lectured to them in their schools and that's how I know how well informed they are. They're thoroughly indoctrinated with product knowledge and know-how. They're also trained in salesmanship. A spirit of experimentation is fine for you during your moments at the counter. But there's one thing you have to realize if you are tempted to buy costly ointment that Cleopatra might have envied. Cleopatra died in her early thirties, so her goos and unguents never really had a chance. Only her mummy knows for sure.

When shopping for cosmetics, I suggest you patronize a counter that has testers so that you can try out the colors on your own skin. Do your beauty shopping at a quiet time of day when the cosmetologist can give you her full attention and other customers are not jostling your elbow. If you're buying cosmetics for a special occasion, take a swatch of the dress you'll be wearing. That way you can match or blend colors without error.

There's one bit of homework you should do before you go shopping. In a very strong, clear light, hold your forearm close to your neck and decide in the mirror, or have a friend help you decide, just where the skin on your wrist or forearm most closely matches in color tones the skin of your neck just below the jawline. It is an advanced professional trick to match face makeup as closely as possible to the skin of your neck. That way you avoid the tell-tale line of demarcation that reveals where your makeup ends and you begin. If you know where on your hand, wrist, mid-arm, or back of the hand the skin best

65

matches the skin of your neck, you have an accurate test area; you can dab on a bit of powder or foundation or rouge at the counter from the tester kit and obtain a fairly accurate notion of how the preparation will look on your face. Don't buy a color because it looks great on the salesgirl. Your naked eye is unable to detect the faint natural rosiness in her complexion that turns a flat beige foundation into a stunning peachy tone. Put that same flat beige on your skin and you may look like an over-exposed veal chop.

When you're buying something new, don't let your sense of economy influence you into taking the large budget size. Make the first one a sample size, even though it may cost a little more percentagewise. If it doesn't work, you can throw it out or give it to your niece without a guilty conscience.

As for testing lipsticks on your hand, my advice is to forget it. You can tell merely by looking at the stick whether it's an orange or a pink or a clear red. But the way it looks at the base of your thumb conveys no clue at all to its appearance on your lips.

JEAN: Virginia, let me tell you how right you are about that. In my cosmetic company days we once took a coral lipstick and put it on a dozen different girls who had very wide variations of natural coloring. Then we lined up all these girls wearing identical lipstick and asked observers, who were also employees of the cosmetic company and therefore extremely knowledgeable about such things, to tell us what color lipstick they thought the girls were wearing. We got ten different answers—ranging from a pale pink to a deep purple. One of the test girls had such naturally deep red, almost ruby lips, that all lipsticks except the strongly whitened ones looked purple on her.

66

VIRGINIA: I know exactly what you mean. I apparently have a prevailing amount of blue in my lips and any lipstick I wear goes dark on me. I also sometimes have trouble with lipstick caking on my mouth.

JEAN: I bet you have that trouble chiefly with the lighter shades. It's true that some of the very light lipsticks do tend to cake on the mouth. But many times it's the wearer's fault. In order to get the intensity of color that she thinks she should have, she puts on more and more lipstick. The lighter the color, the more she puts on. She gets a whole pile-up on her lips, and of course it's going to cake.

VIRGINIA: How do you avoid that?

JEAN: You have to apply your lipstick with a fairly light hand or brush. If you don't get enough depth or intensity of color to satisfy you, don't keep adding more lipstick. Choose instead a lipstick in a darker shade, or one with more intensity of color. You know that if you're using crayon on paper you can't get a light pink to look dark pink by going over and over it. You simply get a big blob of light pink. It's the same with lipstick.

VIRGINIA: But why is it that when you see the young girls with the iridescent, white-mouthed look—why do they want to look like mashed potatoes anyway—their lipstick rarely cakes?

JEAN: Youngsters with flawless skin and smooth young lips get much better results with light lipsticks than do older women with skin that has been lived in a bit. Also, it's a matter of finding a lipstick that works well on your particular lips. Recently I picked up some reduced-price lipsticks in discontinued cases at a drugstore and I was amazed. I could get a smooth, well-defined color effect in a much lighter shade than I usually am able to wear.

VIRGINIA: You just said something interesting, co-author. I know you're a bargain hunter. Do you believe in bargain hunting for cosmetics?

JEAN: I don't believe in bargain hunting in terms of cheaper quality, but I do love to shop for specials; you know, seasonal offerings at half price or a dollar off on products I use regularly. Then, when I'm experimenting with a new look, I start with inexpensive products. For example, a few seasons back the beige look was very big—beige and brown and earth tones in lipstick and rouge and eye makeup. The only way I could figure out whether that look was for me was to buy an assortment of the products in the Five-and-Ten. I learned very quickly that an all-beige makeup made me look like a brown paper bag. I should have known it anyway, for I have light blue eyes and very fair skin. All I have to do is put taupe on my eyelids and strangers come up and say, "May I recommend raw beefsteak for what's happened to your eyes?"

VIRGINIA: I agree completely. But I do feel that for your basic skin-care products—your cleanser or moisture lotion or night cream, or whatever you prefer—you should buy the best you can afford. You might even find that a certain luxury cream that is beyond your ordinary budget does such fabulous things for your particular skin that you're willing to do without something else in order to buy it. And you can always hint at Christmas.

My cream, the one I speak of so fondly, costs exactly one dollar for a good-size jar. So when I say quality, I'm not talking stratosphere and I'm not trying to lure you to the wild products made from elixir of over-sexed hummingbirds. All

I say is that when you find something that's right for you, grab it and stay with it.

Of course, one big problem is the newly improved product. The face cream or eyeshadow or hair spray you've been devoted to for many years suddenly comes out in a new, just unleashed, better-now-than-ever formula. What happens to the old stuff? Is it suddenly terrible? I always wonder because, of course, I've stocked up on sales and will be using the obsolete old formula for at least another year.

Tell me, Jean, what do women really expect from makeup?

JEAN: You have to answer that in categories. In the trade they talk about commodity products. These are grooming aids, like hair spray, nail-polish remover, wave set, deodorant. Women expect chiefly performance from these products. They must do precisely what the copy on the label says. Women are great realists, and they don't want frills or promises, but performance.

At the other end of the scale are the products that offer hope rather than immediate results. These are what the trade calls treatment products: the more expensive night creams and astringents, the rich cleansers, the wrinkle-reducing throat oils. Results are not produced immediately—the women can only hope that tomorrow will be yesterday and the birthday candles will grow backward. This hope is never exactly fulfilled, for life won't stand still.

In a third category are the color products—lipstick, nail enamel, mascara, the whole range of face makeup. A woman applies these and the change is instantly visible. She either likes what she sees, or doesn't.

Of course there is a great deal of overlapping. A five-dollar lipstick with a new moisturizing ingredient and a glorious golden case offers both color and hope that some man will find her lips irresistible.

VIRGINIA: I'm especially interested in the hope category in terms of helping our readers. I can see on one hand where a woman can be led down the primrose path and enticed into spending twenty dollars for a rejuvenating cream that won't help her skin a bit, but will definitely flatten her wallet. On the other hand, it's possible that a woman who has never given herself time before and has cheated herself of the simplest, most basic care, suddenly becomes inspired by the romantic promise of a new miracle face cream. In her determination to have the miracle occur to her, she rediscovers her gender, makes time for proper beauty care, and more than gets her money's worth from that impulsive twenty-dollar splurge.

JEAN: You know, it's odd what a strongly puritanical attitude many people bring to cosmetics. Several years ago when I was giving talks on radio about the behind-the-scenes excitement at the big cosmetics companies, the commentator time and again would pounce with this type of question: "What do you really think of a company that takes two dollars worth of oils and chemicals, puts them in a fancy jar that costs four dollars, adds a bow that costs one dollar, and sells the whole thing to a woman for thirty dollars?"

I suppose they wanted me to say it was a disgrace and there should be a law. But I always countered by asking: "What about the woman who pays six hundred dollars for a Dior suit that is made of only forty dollars worth of material and buttons? If she wants a six hundred dollar suit on her back and a thirty dollar cream on her dressing table . . ."

VIRGINIA: Wait a minute. Are you talking about cosmetics as status symbols?

JEAN: Of course I am. Many women today find it most important to pay a premium price for a chic lipstick to take out of their bags or a prestige cream to decorate their dressing tables. It tells the world, in the strange shorthand of our time, how much their husbands cherish them.

VIRGINIA: That may be, or does it announce to what lengths they have to go to hold onto their men?

Anyway, to get back to what goes on across the counter, I cannot criticize the salesgirl, because this is her way of making a living. Just as your choice between one make of automobile and another may depend on salesmanship, so sales skill may be the factor in directing you to a particular brand of cosmetics. I admire the hours of training these girls go through, their thorough product knowledge, their understanding of women's needs.

There is only one thing I want to caution you about. There is something about the penetrating eye of the cosmetologist that may make you feel you must go in for complete skin scraping and surgery. You have to learn to hold your ground. If she looks at you and is able to discover a new dry area that has you wondering how you had the courage to walk to the store with this terrible condition, and you feel that all the women in sight are nudging each other and saying, "Oh, she's dry! She's dry!" you have to be able to look back and search for *her* dry area. Your best gamesmanship is to look for defects—her tiny eye wrinkles that have not been taken away by the cream she is trying to sell you, the slight crepiness of her lids that is accentuated by the shadow she is urging you to buy. Count her failings as aggressively as she counts yours. That's your best counter-attack.

10

On the Scent of Beauty

The average woman who works around the house has her own wardrobe of perfume—detergents, soaps, silver polishes—she doesn't lack for aromas. But naturally she wants the joy and delight of a lovely personal scent with her all the time. I may be going against the tide, but I think your perfume should be very different from your way of life. If you're a very outdoorsy, athletic type, you shouldn't wear tweedy or heathery scents. If you're the clinging, very sweet type, your fragrance should not be cloying and overly floral. The perfume should be a release of the hidden you, and it should offer contrast to the you that is visible to all observers.

I feel also that you should change perfumes from time to time, especially when you become immune to your own scent and are no longer aware of it. I am in favor of almost any kind of change that awakens the senses and gives them new awareness. When you find a new scent, stay with it for a while. Make it yours. Then maybe in a few years you will be ready for another change of pace.

We do associate aromas with people. Now Lilo, the enchanting Broadway and TV star, finds that Arpège is magnificent on her. Yet another woman wearing it, or any other perfume, may not get the same fantastic effect. Our own body chemistry gives each perfume we use a different impact and value. For myself, I love Detchema and Cabochard and Mme. Rochas. Some of my close friends are devoted to Miss Dior, Shalimar, Joy, Imprèvu.

You find a beautiful fragrance by using the tester bottles in drugstores and department stores. You put the scent on your wrist or arm. You walk around for several hours, smelling the scented spot at frequent intervals to see how long your body holds the fragrance. If someone smiles at you in an elevator, or if when you get home someone says, "What have you got on? It's delightful!" then you go back and buy it.

I thought I knew just about all the ways there are to wear perfume until I checked with the Fragrance Foundation and became conscious of my shortcomings. The Fragrance Foundation, dedicated to the wider and more enjoyable use of scent, must keep its experts awake all night dreaming up new ways to use perfume and toilet water. First they would have you know that perfume is the longest lasting and most intensive form of fragrance. Next in line is toilet water. Cologne is usually the lightest. Scented bath oils, which have recently risen to great popularity, have extraordinary clinging power. Many of them also smooth and moisturize your skin.

Perfume is best applied to pulse spots on the skin—back of the ears, at the throat, at the wrist. Since my skin tends not to hold perfume for very long I take a bit of cotton, saturate it with perfume or toilet water, and tuck it into my bra. Used that way, my scent lasts for hours and pervades the air. Perfume lasts longer on you in summer than in winter. It tends to have less staying power on cold, crisp winter days. It is more enduring if your skin is oily.

Toilet water and cologne may be applied more lavishly than perfume. On hot, miserable days, you can splash them on with a free hand. Use an atomizer to mist yourself completely. But avoid spraying furs—they may stain. Perfume should not be hoarded, for time and too much light do not deal kindly with the fragile balance of essential oils.

If you want a dozen or so fresh and original ways to use fragrance, start with these:

Scent your letters by spraying with an aerosol before sending.

Spray your closet with fragrance right after cleaning. It will give your clothes and your linens a springlike freshness.

Put empty bottles in your sweater drawer to get the last whisper of remaining scent.

Add a few drops of fragrance to the water when you rinse your lingerie.

Put a few drops of fragrance on a light bulb and let the aroma diffuse through the room.

Sprinkle toilet water on the lining of your handbags and on your hatbands.

Spray air conditioners with cologne for scented fresh air.

Spray your ironing board with fragrance before pressing blouses, handkerchiefs, scarves, and curtains.

Use cologne on your hair as a quick wave set.

A gentle rubbing of cologne on tired feet will refresh them on a hot summer day.

Spray cologne on artificial flowers.

Spray padded clothes hangers with cologne.

Use perfumed candles to set the mood for a party.

I've been teaching my little granddaughter about perfume, and have given her an atomizer to play with. But she's been told not to spray the boy she plays with in the park. And I suggest that if you have a little boy, you don't encourage him to fool around with your perfume. We're having enough trouble with boys as it is.

11

Under the Dryer

If I were writing a history book I would classify the beauty salon as one of the most valuable innovations of the twentieth century. It is the greatest boon to the American woman since the abolition of tight corseting. I remember back when I was a very little girl, Irene Castle, the great dancer, bobbed her hair and had a marcel wave. My mother, who was far more adventurous than I realized then, came home one day, her long, long tresses clipped short. My father almost fainted. I begged my mother to take me along the next time she had her hair cut.

76

Under the Dryer

In those days the beauty parlor was still in its transition stage from the barber shop. If you believe in the Darwinian theory, you will find that the beauty shop as we knew it followed the evolution of the curler. In the beginning hair was curled with a hot iron, a weapon of injury which might be more useful in commando tactics than some of our current weapons. Suddenly in the barber shops there were chairs for ladies, where operators wielded scissors and iron. Everything was antiseptic and white and germicidal. I was fascinated by the fact that they would wash a head of hair, have it come out looking like a dead rat, wet and stringy, and then all of a sudden an absolute wizard would push waves into this wet head with his fingers. After that the customer would go into a contraption for which she should really have been required to notify her next of kin—that's how scary the early dryers were.

There sat Mama, going from shades of pink to deep red to molten purple. Finally, out she came, and that same wizard took a comb and combed beauty into her hair. Now my mother is a ravishingly beautiful woman, but nobody looks good with wet hair. I fell in love right then and there with the idea that there are people whose hands can mold beauty for you. As the years progressed I became familiar with beauty parlors on my own, and my whole life changed when I became blond.

Inside of me all through my early years was this tremendous desire to be a blond. I was a thickset brunette then—big-boned was the horrid word they used. I think it meant that I had a big amount of fat over my bones. But most of all I wanted to be a blond. At that time I was at a very strict girls' boarding school. We weren't allowed dates. When a boy came to call, a hostess sat right there with you and rang a buzzer if you

77

said anything unsuitable. My friends thought there was a fire drill whenever a boy came to see me.

I was utterly bored with all the restrictions and with myself. One Monday I went into Washington, D.C. It was then the era of "nice-girls-don't-do-this," and the thing they didn't do most of all was dye their hair. But I didn't care. I went to a downtown beauty salon. Now it is imperative for your first beauty operator to have a moustache. Mr. Pierre or Mr. Louis may have come from Trenton or Hackensack, but his moustache immediately gives you the feeling he is French. I had enough hair then for rental. Some people could give blood—I could give hair. The trouble was that all this hair was a brown color I hated. I couldn't stand it.

"You want to be a blond?" Mr. Pierre asked. "What color?"

I said, "Exactly like Jean Harlow."

"This is going to take time," he said.

I was there for seven hours. I sat and looked at my face for seven hours. Of course there is nothing in the world more disfiguring than having a bleach put on. A Zulu becomes Miss America by comparison. Each little root was doused with liquid white, which ran down. You wore glasses in those days—goggles, really—to protect your eyes. I guess I should have fastened my seat belt, too.

After seven hours I emerged with white blond hair. White, like Snow White. But I got rid of the biggest problem of my life that day and probably saved myself from an analyst's couch.

I didn't like being a brunette. I didn't like my type. I didn't like what I was. I didn't feel girl-like. And I didn't like the boys' attitude toward me. But now, suddenly, it was all changed. I walked down the street and if anyone didn't look at me, I looked at him. And I whistled. And I danced. I had ball bearings in my soul.

Of course when I got back to school the dean took one look at me and I was on the critical list for two months. I was allowed breathing privileges at night, but nothing else. She called my father in Chicago immediately. Papa, with that marvelous wisdom of his—he was the one who unlocked all beauty for me, beauty of the soul, beauty of the mind, beauty of self-belief—called me.

"How are you, darling?" he asked.

"Oh, fine."

"What's new? How do you look? Are you still on your diet?"

"Oh, yes, I've lost twenty-five pounds."

"That's fine. How do you look? How's your hair?"

"Oh," I said, "I'm a blond."

"Oh, you are," as if this were the first time he was hearing it. "What made you do that? I thought you had beautiful hair."

"Papa, I didn't like it. My hair made me feel drab. It pulled me down. Now I feel like a bird about to fly."

"Then keep it that way," he said.

That's what I mean when I say *confidence and security*. My father's confidence in me gave me the security to see beauty.

The change to blond released inside of me an awful lot that needed to get out. I didn't like my type, and through cosmetic techniques I was able to develop into someone who was really there all the time but was hidden deep inside me. So the beauty parlor became my friend at a very early age.

I think that at certain times of every woman's life she should visit a beauty parlor. We are not going to tell you to go once a week, twice a week, or any other schedule, because this is a time when the finest products are available to you to use right in your home. But beyond the skill a professional can give you, which is self-explanatory, there are marvels that the beauty parlor does for your ego. During the few hours that you are there, someone is thinking solely about you—not about your daughter, not your son, not your mother, not your neighbor—it's nobody but you they are concentrating on. Someone washes your hair, brushes your hair, gives it a treatment, massages your scalp as you lie back. Every dish you own can be in the sink. You don't care. This is your particular time, when someone looks at your face in the mirror, gives you what he thinks is the most becoming hair style, combs it out, and grants you your moment of beauty.

I can't overemphasize the value of choosing the right beauty parlor. It should not be too crowded. The people who work there should have personal regard for you. If it is in a large city, it should not depend on transient trade. The operator you choose should be there week after week, should get to know you, get to know your way of life, what your husband likes, and how far he or she can go in creating a new style or color. There is unbelievable therapy in going to a beauty parlor and allowing someone to suggest, perhaps, a new makeup or a new way of emphasizing your eyes.

We've asked each other a thousand times while working on this book: How does a woman know what she's really like? Well, one way to find out is for you to establish the kind of relationship you really should have with your beauty operator. She or he can tell you more about yourself than anybody in the world. You can honestly say to your operator, "I don't want to look like the woman next to me, but what type am I?"

Your operator has gone to beauty school and has been

taught hair styles in accordance with the structure of the face. This person, seeing you with your hair wet and looking your worst, pulls back your hair and then honestly says to you, "Look, madam, you have a full chin. Your neck is not long. Your face is square." Take it from him with love, for he speaks from knowledge. That's the person to whom you should go to find out what your type is. Let him style for you according to your face, and let him help you in your makeup. You'll never find anybody who will give you more integrity and more personal thought than your beautician, if you have faith in him.

So in choosing your beauty parlor, make sure it is updated. Don't be afraid of the very young. This is one business where the very young who are fresh from school, if they have talented hands, may be geniuses one year after graduation. The fact that someone has been in the business for years is not necessarily an advantage—unless he's been doing great work for his customers all these years. And get someone who really takes time out to look at you and tell you who you are. You don't have to settle for the neighborhood shop if it is not the best. You don't have to follow your friends and patronize the big name in town if you find he doesn't take time to look at you and see you clearly.

One of the things I dislike most is the once-a-week beauty. Between salon appointments she looks as if she's just come from a sickbed. You should never wear a hair style you can't handle yourself. You should never wear a hair style that is so set it makes you unapproachable for two days and then leaves you looking like a waif in the rain for the other five. You should never wear anything that makes you rigid and uncomfortable. the style should never wear you.

81

A long time ago I went to my beauty parlor and I paid the beautician to teach me how to dry-set my hair and comb it out between professional settings. I've met women (if they had been driving the covered wagons the West would never have been found) who are so helpless. They flutter and murmur, "I just can't do it."

You're darn tootin' you can do it! Nobody's any unhandier than I was. But my desire for beauty was greater than my physical limitations. And here are some of the things I've learned, just to get you started. Number one: hairpins don't work. They just don't hold the hair at night. I use rollers and bobby pins, and have constant scalp abrasions to prove my diligence. If you want your hair to look soft and natural and lovely when your husband comes home for dinner, pins or rollers during the day are your best answer. But they're not to be worn out in the community, or anywhere you will be observed by another human being. Sponge rollers, the soft rollers you can sleep on, have proved very valuable to me. And then there's the curling iron, which is undergoing something of a revival. Several of my friends have become very skillful with the electric curling iron, to the extent that they rely on it solely, between settings.

I'm assuming, of course, that you go to a professional stylist for the line and shape you want. Then you take care of it yourself with dry settings. I do not recommend wetting the hair for at-home resettings during the week. I use rollers on the side and bobby pins on top. When you put your hair up, take a straight, long piece of chiffon—at least a yard long—fold it lengthwise into two or three thicknesses and wrap it around your head, starting at the back and crisscrossing it in the front. Then take it around again to the back and fasten

it with a pin, or put a hook on it. It's the crisscross in front
that makes it look like a turban, and the height of the rollers
will make the scarf stand up. The scarf is far more flattering
than raggedy hair hanging down, and more becoming than
a net.

Once you've chosen an operator you might want to tell
him what we're doing in St. Louis and in several other cities
around the country. Women in St. Louis pay a fee to their hair
stylist to give them a series of eight or ten lessons on how to
set their hair dry. He teaches them how to set and comb out
their hair between professional hair appointments. If your
hairdresser insists upon doing your hair in a style that you can't
possibly take care of between visits, I'd say you should give
him up and find someone who can work with you more flexibly
and appreciate your problem of between-visits maintenance. I
myself would never patronize a hairdresser who sets my hair
in a way I can't handle.

We've been discussing set, but the key to a becoming style
is cut, and here I think most of us are in agreement that a
professional touch is needed. Few of us are presumptuous
enough to cut and style our own hair, and I'm afraid that most
of those who do are fooling no one. At the same time that
we may save a few dollars, we are setting ourselves up as
local eccentrics: "Yes, Bess is such a sweet woman, but why
does she insist on cutting her own hair?" What's more, there
is a brand new artistry involved today in styling short hair.
It began when Vidal Sassoon moved from London to New
York and introduced some of the most chic young women in
town to the look of fresh, youthful, geometric cuts. Not every
woman is able to stand the severe test of Sassoon's geometry.
But the new emphasis on cutting techniques using blunt

83

cuts, diagonal cuts, and contouring cuts has opened a whole new area of styling for the woman who wants to wear her hair fairly close to the head in a coiffure that practically arranges itself with a toss or shake of the head between cutting sessions.

As for hair color, if your beauty parlor isn't up on the latest colors and the latest coloring techniques, then you're in the wrong place. How do you know what's the latest? You pick up a fashion magazine and flip through the illustrations and the ads; you watch the commercials on television for product demonstrations. Within hours you can become your own expert on what's new. If you can learn so quickly, imagine what sources of information are open to a beautician, who is offered seminars every few weeks by the leading hair color companies and who is invited to regional shows where new beauty products and methods are thoroughly demonstrated. If your beautician does not avail himself of the latest, and insists upon relying on the knowledge he picked up ten or fifteen years ago, it's time for you to change beauty parlors.

The girl at the reception desk of your salon can make you feel either like Mrs. Vanderbilt or like Cinderella without feet, let alone shoes. She is really one of the beauty parlor's most valuable assets. She sets the pace: spaces appointments, determines whether work runs smoothly or piles up into exasperating delays. Anyway, you get past the receptionist, either with a smile or with a cold stare, and put on the smock. This is the leveler of all women. You take off your jewelry, your hair comes down—it's dirty and a little oily, that's why you're there. If it's tinted, the roots are growing out. You sit down, and while you're waiting for your operator, you start to talk to the women around you. You talk about the most personal things. There's something about the hair-down posture that invites intimacy, even with strangers. Then you get into the chair, have your hair washed and set, spend time under the dryer, and when you've had the comb-out, although you're the same woman who has just spent hours confiding your inmost secrets, you suddenly walk out without even saying good-bye. You've taken on this whole new personality from having your hair done. I frankly liked you better under the dryer, but your new aloofness is part of the lift you get from going to the beauty parlor.

I've had experiences in beauty parlors that you wouldn't believe. I used to go to a shop owned by a woman who had four dogs and four chairs. The dogs sat on the chairs and the customers stood up. Another time, both the mistress and the wife of a fairly prominent man turned up simultaneously for beauty appointments at the same place. Everyone knew about the situation except, naturally, the wife. In this case it happened that the girl friend was not clued-in either. Suddenly there was a phone call. The two women both got out from under their dryers. While everyone else in the place froze, the owner collected his presence of mind, went over to the girl and said, "We said Mrs. *Herbert* Taylor, not Mrs. *Howard* Taylor." The girl caught on, disappeared with the owner into his office, came out a few minutes later, put on her coat and a kerchief over her rollers, muttered something about "I have to go out and get something; I'll be right back," and, I heard, reappeared for her comb-out several hours later, when the wife was safely gone.

In some beauty parlors women walk about with bleach on their upper lips, depilatories on their legs, false nail clamps on their fingers, wisps of hair wrapped in foil and pulled through holes in plastic frosting caps. They look like some-

thing from Mars and you expect them to say, "Take me to
your leader." Yet they walk around perfectly at ease, chatting
with friends, asking perfect strangers what they're knitting.
That's the wonderful thing about women—they're comfortable
only when they're at their absolute best or their utter worst.

12

More under the Dryer

The beauty shop I patronized in Washington as a girl was already a far cry from that anti-fungus establishment of my childhood. It was pink and gold and warm with the perfume and chatter of smart women. Beauty was coming into its own, and, for the first time in the history of America, women of all classes, not just the wealthy and highborn but all women, from the scrubwoman on, could find beauty within the realm of the possible.

At this stage women were all trying to look alike. There was conformity born of the end of isolation. Newspapers, magazines, the movies, all set styles and trends. Women on farms and in small towns had access to the same beauty examples as sophisticated city girls, and small wonder every woman wanted to be Jean Harlow or Carole Lombard. With communication came the banding together of women. The gain was the opening of doors; the loss, the destruction of individuality through the slavish imitation of movie stars.

Women everywhere had pencil-thin eyebrows, tight, ridiculous little mouths that had nothing to do with their own mouths, over-crimped hair, a gash of red lipstick against over-pale skin. I think this conformity has been a devastating thing. Its ill effects continue right to this day. Customers still look at the woman in the next chair and say, "I'll have what she has." That's all right for ordering at a restaurant—but not in a beauty parlor.

Let me say one thing: I don't believe very strongly in marble floors, bronze fixtures, and upholstery straight from Versailles; I go to a beauty parlor for work. Of course I want it to be clean. I don't mind those with open floor plans where everyone brushes up against everyone else. I enjoy mingling with people and I find an awful lot of material about life from relaxed strangers. Other women, on the other hand, are miserable unless they have privacy in their own little booths. So you have to know yourself.

Back during World War II, when I was working for the Red Cross, I recall my father made me a present of my first mink coat, and I was excited beyond belief. A mink was an even more thrilling thing to get in those days than it is today. I was in a beauty parlor and just as I was being combed out I got a call that I was needed at Mitchell Field, then the headquarters of our Red Cross unit. I grabbed my coat and rushed out.

When I got to Mitchell Field I changed into my uniform in the dark. Not until I was released from the field hours later did I discover that I was wearing not a dress-length coat, but a three-quarter length jacket. I had taken the wrong coat. Well, I couldn't call the shop—it had been closed for hours—so I took good care of the coat overnight and phoned the shop the first thing in the morning. The other woman had been calling the owner at home every ten minutes all night demanding that something be done. It turned out she was a midget, at least compared to me. While her full-length coat was only a jacket on me, my coat on her was sweeping the floor and flapping against her ankles. I told the shopowner to let her know that I had her coat. She called me. "Have you been sitting on my coat?" she demanded.

I said, "I beg your pardon?"

She said, "My coat. Have you been sitting on it?"

I said, "Well, I can't stand up to drive, so I guess I was sitting down in it."

She said, "Well, I'm coming with my furrier to inspect that coat, and if the pelt has been ruined, you'll have to pay."

I said, "Fine. You can have your furrier look at my coat at the same time. I hear you've been cleaning the street with it."

She said, "Nothing of the kind. Can I help it if it was too long?"

I said, "No more than I can help it if yours was too short."

She arrived with her furrier, and I know how King Solomon must have felt when the two mothers were claiming the child. The furrier looked at her coat, whispered to her, they both pushed their fingers into the fur and blew on the pelts. By this time my coat wasn't looking so good to me. But finally, with a sneer and in a vicious tone, she said, "All right, I don't think you've ruined it."

When you go to a beauty salon you should choose one that is patronized by women who lead the same kind of life that you do. If you are a suburban housewife and want an uncomplicated but becoming look, then go to someone who specializes in your needs. Don't travel fifty miles to a city shop that does high fashion models who can stop by every morning for a comb-out. If you have a tight schedule, go to someone who respects your time and his own and adheres to his appointment book. If you have a definite budget, select a place that does not insist on selling you services you can't afford.

You must take into consideration the workmanship you need, the environment. Do you seek relaxation in a salon or speed? To me, the only relaxation I get in my life is my beauty salon. I adore it. The one I go to is like Grand Central Terminal at rush hour before a holiday weekend. There are no separate booths and everyone has everything done in full view of everyone else. Customers march around with bleach on their hair to visit with friends. The woman next to you is practically having a pedicure in your lap. The woman under the first dryer is brushing her poodle. Another is crying hysterically because she has just broken up with her boy friend. The whole thing is a carnival and I love it. But I've had friends who have gone to my beauty salon on my recommendation and they've had to enter into deep therapy for years just from that one visit. The whole atmosphere makes them frantically nervous, but I find it very funny.

You have to know your own temperament. If you want privacy, a little room to yourself, quiet elegance, a tiptoe atmosphere, then by all means find a salon that gives you these features.

Naturally you must choose a beautician whose taste is similar to yours. For all her skill, she may have a more flamboyant personality than yours and she may be at her best when dressing hair into daring and spectacular confections. Don't engage in a war of nerves with her, and don't give up beauty salons altogether. Quietly shift to another shop or another operator to find greater compatibility of temperament. You have a right to have your beautician respect your needs. If you don't like a big fluffy head or teasing or lots of spray, you should speak out and your wishes should be followed.

Sometimes I think there should be rules for customers, too. One of my least favorite types is the woman who doesn't even wait until she leaves to start redoing her hair, right in front of the beautician. I admit that a beautician may sometimes out-style you. But don't you go into the place looking for a change, looking for the real you? Then the moment you see something a little bit different from the old you, why start tearing it down? It's unwise not to give your hair stylist a chance.

There's also a financial angle in choosing a beauty parlor. Many women feel beauty has become overpriced. They can't afford it. Their child needs this, their mother needs that. To me this is a most hazardous attitude. When a woman feels that her needs are last on the hit parade, she is in very bad shape. Don't forget, these are two hours, the only two hours in the week when you can walk away from responsibilities, burdens, demands, telephones, worries. For the brief period of your visit you put yourself in the hands of someone who is concentrating only on you and your needs. I think this is truly great preventive therapy. It is an ego-builder, vitamin C for Care, vitamin L for Love, and as far as I'm concerned, the quickest way to send the psychiatrists to the poorhouse.

Many women are afraid they will be sold things against their will—color, rinse, or conditioner. Obviously, a salon that over-sells or high-pressures is to be avoided. But think what you spend to thoroughly clean your house in the fall and spring, to provide slipcovers for your furniture, to keep your silver shin-ing and your crystal sparkling! And then you do not care enough to give proper maintenance to your own hair and face, the only irreplaceable possessions you have. There is no second chance for hair or skin that has been abused. So I can't state strongly enough that you must take the beauty parlor out of the realm of occasional luxuries and make it a steady essential of your life. A once-a-week visit or the equivalent in time at home is like a premium on an insurance policy—a policy of liv-ing insurance you cannot afford to have lapse. The biggest bank loan in the world will not buy back beauty lost through abuse or extreme neglect.

I believe that if you were to sit and talk to your husband and let him read this chapter, you might reach a new understanding. Let him know what a compliment it is to him that you want to look well; let him know that your appearance is a reflection of your happiness with him, his ability to take care of his fam-ily, his appreciation of you at your best.

Whenever I go to a party and meet an attractive man, my eyes begin to rove to find out which woman is his wife. If she's a dowdy-looking frump, with bad taste in clothes and poorly gotten together, something happens to my opinion of him. That may be very unkind of me, because he may have a problem with her. Or she may be totally preoccupied with some work and feel that personal adornment is a vanity she's not entitled to. Even so, I judge the stature of a man by the appearance of his wife. Remember, an awful lot of other people do, too.

Now I have a footnote for beauty salon owners who might be reading this book. I'm not going to go into the conduct of quite a number of receptionists and the lack of happy eagerness with which they greet you and the lack of punctuality of some operators, for this is a book for the consumer, not the proprietor. But one thing I would like to say at this point is that one of the most demoralizing things to a woman when she gets to a salon is being stripped of her clothes, which she has put on with a certain care. Then she must don the most unbecoming, shop-worn, color-faded smock in the world. Some of the smocks I've worn have made me feel like a rejected CARE package; I've never seen such hideous things. If you're tall, they always come only halfway to the knee. If Courrèges or Mary Quant think they have discovered the new short length, they have not seen certain women in smocks.

There should be sizes in smocks, lengths, and, if you are a regular patron, there should be a service that permits you to bring your own and leave it there. You wouldn't mind in the least paying a minimal charge for laundry. Whenever I tell a salon owner what a mistake I think he is making in putting his customers in those no-color or awful seersucker wrappers, he tells me about laundry problems. Well, I can tell him about customer problems, if he doesn't do something about those smocks.

13

All about Hair

If you think I'm going to tell you how to style your hair and how to color it, you're wrong. I can't give that kind of advice long distance! You have to look in the mirror, read the magazines and newspapers, talk to your hairdresser, talk to the cosmetician in your drug store or department store, talk to your husband, maybe talk to your teenage children (if you're on speaking terms with them), and then make your own decision.

Everything's out there waiting for you—marvelous new products designed by cosmetic chemists to color your hair temporarily or permanently, at home or in the salon, at budget prices or "the sky's the limit." There's even a fabulous new machine that looks like a dryer and cuts down coloring time in a salon to nearly nothing—one minute under the machine is equal to about five minutes of ordinary coloring time. That means that a color which normally takes half an hour to develop does its job in just six minutes if you sit under the machine. So you don't even have the excuse of no time!

While I won't write you a prescription for your hair, I have shared with you throughout this book my philosophy about hair style and hair color—you can't possibly have missed the message. And now I'm going to share with you my notebook of hair facts that I have gathered through the years from my many friends in the beauty field and from beauty operators all over the country. Every time I learned something new about hair, I jotted it down. I may be telling you more than you care to know, but here goes:

Hair grows faster from March to July than from August to February, and faster by day than by night.

New hair grows at a rate of approximately ⅜ to ¾ of an inch per month.

As the hair gets longer, this rapid growth slows down gradually.

When the hair is very long, the rate of growth is so slow that it takes about six weeks of growth before any additional length can be measured.

There are about 1,000 hairs per square inch of scalp. The average area of adult scalp is 120 square inches, thus the average adult has about 120,000 individual scalp hairs.

The finer the hair, the more hairs grow in a given area. Blond hairs, usually the finest, are the most numerous. Brunettes have fewer individual hairs than blonds, and redheads have the fewest hairs of all.

A single hair is exceptionally elastic. It can stretch some 45 percent of its length and can support a weight of two to six ounces before it breaks.

The exact dimension of a single hair varies with the texture. The diameter of a single hair can range from $\frac{1}{1500}$ to $\frac{1}{40}$ of an inch.

Healthy hair depends on general health. Often, a person whose hair has a natural gloss finds that the hair becomes dull and drab during even a minor illness of a few days' duration.

The skin is constantly shedding dead cells. Scales from parts of the body other than the scalp are rubbed off by the friction of clothing and by washing. They disappear in the air or the bath water and are seldom noticed. Scales from the scalp, however, are held by the hairs and can be very noticeable, especially in abnormal quantities. This is called dandruff.

Some slight dandruff is completely normal. Severe cases are not only unsightly, but also can lead to hair loss. A good dandruff treatment shampoo rids the scalp of dandruff.

Many people think that frequent washing "dries" the hair. Actually, washing stimulates secretions from the oil glands opening into the hair follicles. Too hot a shampoo may overstimulate oily hair.

If washed with the proper shampoo and dried properly, hair may be washed as often as one wishes with no ill effects. If you live in a sooty city your hair will probably need washing every five or six days.

Experimentation has shown that the tensile strength of hair

is considerably less when wet; consequently, the hair breaks more easily when it is wet.

Fine hair, the most difficult kind to handle, snarls easily, is resistant to curl, and lacks body. A *creme* rinse that has been designed to give body to fine hair coats each hair shaft with a special protein formula that gives it added substance. Unlike regular creme rinses that leave naturally soft and delicate fine hair even more limp, a creme rinse with body actually helps *add* body and fullness as it smooths away tangles and knots.

Tiny muscles run out from the hair follicles. When you're frightened or cold, these muscles contract, giving a prickly sensation; thus the expression, "My hair stood on end."

Hair is a poor conductor of heat, and therefore it protects against exposure to the rays of the sun. It also keeps in the natural body heat when the head is exposed to the cold.

The hair on the head forms a cushion that protects against injury, and thus is a splendid defense to the skull in the case of falls or blows. It also serves as an excellent filter and traps nearly all dirt which comes in contact with it.

Hair is subject to the same laws of heredity as any other physical characteristic. Individuals of the same family are usually alike in possessing scanty or abundant hair, coarse or fine hair.

If the hair on your head were woven into a slender rope it could support a suspended weight of two thousand pounds—heavier than that of a small car.

An individual hair lives two to five years. Then the follicle that produced it shrinks and the hair drops out. When the follicle returns to action, a new hair grows. At all times, about 10 percent of the scalp follicles are resting.

Normal daily hair loss is about eighty hairs.

If your hair is very coarse and unruly there are special rinses that will help tame it.

If your hair has been abused it may need a protein conditioner.

If your hair is discolored from lake scum or chlorine in a swimming pool, you can get it back into shape with a heavy oil conditioner.

If your hair is unusually resistant to color it will respond better if it is lightened first to presoften it, then colored.

Lightened or colored hair should be protected from the sun; wear a hat or scarf.

You normally should not use spray to create the structure of a hair style. (An elaborate fantasy style for evening is something else again.) The best-looking styles are only moderately sprayed after the first comb-out. You can use a touch of spray when combing and arranging your hair daily. On the last day before your regular shampoo, you may have to spray hard to keep the set in place.

Hair looks best if it is dried with a temperate rather than a hot setting of the dryer. The last five minutes of drying should be at a cooler temperature, to help settle the outer layer of the hair and make it more resilient.

Hair worn long from the crown with curl on the ends gives a droopy, old-fashioned look and emphasizes downward lines on the face, unless you're under twenty. A mature woman should not wear her hair long and draggy. If it is worn with a little height on top and some width at about eye level, it will draw attention away from a sagging jaw line to pretty eyes.

Don't buy cheap combs. If they are badly finished, they can cut and tear your hair. Use a roomy shower cap—it will protect your styling. Your best bet for a brush is the hairdresser type. The back is about one inch to 1¾ inches wide, and bristles fan out from both sides.

If your hair is very fine, try setting it in beer . . . have a blunt cut . . . don't wear it long . . . don't style it with little points.

If your hair is too curly, use a special creme rinse and setting lotion. You can have it straightened—but not more often than every six months. Set it on very fat rollers. Wear it very short or fairly long so that the weight will pull out the excessive curl. If you lighten it you will find it much easier to control.

The truth about teasing: Teasing with a metal comb can break your hair, particularly if it has been lightened. Teasing is matting your hair, forming it into a bird's nest under the top smooth layer by heavy backward combing from the end of the hair toward the scalp. Teasing may be necessary if you are wearing your hair in a style that needs a solid layer to lift the hair away from the head.

Back combing or back brushing is lightly brushing or combing the hair from the end toward the scalp to enmesh it gently and give airiness and lift to the style.

If you've tinted or lightened your hair and then decided not to stay with the color, don't just stop coloring or you'll have to live for months with two-color hair. You can color the lightened part back to the original color. Or, if you're more than 50 percent gray, use a temporary brown rinse on the gray part as it grows in, until you are ready to cut off the permanently colored part. Frequent shampooing will speed the decoloring process.

Now you can amaze your friends with what you know about hair. But for goodness sakes, don't just stand there with your tired hair drooping and graying and telling the world you've given up. Do something!

There's something I did recently which has made a great difference in my life and my coiffure. I bought myself a fall. A fall, as you know, is a partial wig, an arrangement of someone else's hair that you attach to your own head and pass off as part of your own coiffure.

I was never really a wig woman. I felt that a wig tended to emphasize the laziness and indolence of the woman who figured she could get away without brushing, washing, or coloring her hair by popping a wig over her messy locks. I didn't think that was psychologically good for women. I will admit though, that for women who have lost their hair or who have severely damaged hair or who have absolutely unmanageable hair, a wig is often a great joy. Well, a fall is all that and more so.

At this moment my hair is multiple shades of blond. Now I sleep on the back of my head and I look like half a picture when I get up in the morning. My hair is high in the front, and there isn't anything there at all in the back. So I had a fall made, matched precisely in color to my dark and light blond. It is mounted on a piece of net about the size of a small doily. I anchor the net with half a dozen hairpins at the back of my head—I make sure it's well anchored in case of a tailwind. Then I just brush or comb the fall into my own hair. It fills in the hollow in back of my head and gives height and shape to my coiffure. With the fall, I've been able to go as many as ten days between washings and my hair has looked fine. I take the fall with me to the salon and my operator washes and sets it while I am sitting under the dryer. I've only had it colored once. But anytime I change my own hair color, the fall goes right along.

All about Hair

I recommend a fall rather than a wig to women everywhere. It gives body to your hair, excitement to your hairdo, and a sense of fun to your whole life. The next time you're at your beauty parlor or at the hair counter of a department store, let yourself get talked into a fall. You'll enjoy every minute of it.

14

Shears and Cheers

I was in Illinois last summer, appearing at the Pheasant Run Playhouse in St. Charles, and went to Chicago to have my hair done. I think I approached this appointment with more apprehension than a bride does her second wedding night. You get so used to a hairdresser that to change is almost impossible. But I found living proof of the old adage, "No one is irreplaceable," when I entered the salon of Mr. Fredrick Glaser. It is called Fred's Shears & Cheers. The name itself shows the highest optimism, because most women do not feel like cheering after they have been sheared—I mean financially and physically. I talked to Mr. Fredrick and this is what happened.

VIRGINIA: Fred, you are one of the highest-priced hair stylists in America. How do you have the nerve to do this in a city as conservative as Chicago?

FRED: Well, in addition to styling hair, I have other interests in the beauty and fashion fields. To cut down my daily clientele and allow more time for my other interests, I set a price of twenty-five dollars for a shampoo and set. Instead of discouraging bookings, I found it appealed to women as something special, and we were flooded with clients from all over. Suddenly I was being booked every half hour again.

VIRGINIA: Do you think it's your ability or the snob appeal of the price?

FRED: When we first started the new price, a few women ventured in for snob appeal. But when they had been in the salon a while they realized there was much more to it than a simple shampoo and set. Suddenly I was involving them in all my other interests, and they were getting a larger view of the whole fashion industry.

VIRGINIA: Why is it that a woman will take so much—well, almost abuse—from a male hairdresser and depend so completely on his judgment, and won't from a female hairdresser?

FRED: I think women are basically jealous of each other. No matter how talented a female operator is, she will never do as well on another woman as she would on herself.

VIRGINIA: When a woman buys an expensive dress, she certainly does not want to see another woman wearing the same dress. Since you charge such a stiff price, is there a way to assure an individually designed hair style at that price?

FRED: I create for the image the customer wants to project.

103

I take the time to analyze the woman, find out certain facts, such as whether she wears designer clothes, and then I style the hair exclusively for her.

VIRGINIA: To what lengths do you allow your clients to dictate their hair styles to you?

FRED: They come to me to be styled; they don't come to give directions. They could go to a technician for that.

VIRGINIA: Have you ever absolutely refused to give a woman something she has asked for?

FRED: I have. It happened just recently. A woman came to me and tried to direct me. She shouldn't have come to me in the first place; she should have gone to a technician. I am a designer.

VIRGINIA: How many designers are there in America today?

FRED: Very few.

VIRGINIA: What should be the elements that go into an individual design? When you look at a woman what are the things you consider before you design a coiffure for her? What physical features do you analyze? How do you decide what is right? I am asking this question because so many do-it-yourself magazines tell a woman to look at herself and see what type she is. I would like a few pointers to help the woman do this.

FRED: First, I want to say there are very few competent designers in this country today. You have to have a great deal of heart to design.

VIRGINIA: Heart?

FRED: Empathy. You have to understand people first and design later. Without heart, you cannot do it. You have to love and understand people first.

VIRGINIA: Then you would say it is psychological as well as physical?

104

FRED: Yes. You don't design the hair, you are really designing the mind.

VIRGINIA: Getting back to the question of how a woman should look at herself to find out what type she is, what do you look for in a client and how can a woman transfer this to her own mirror?

FRED: I'd say it's hard for a woman to analyze herself; that is why we have professional people.

VIRGINIA: What if she cannot afford salon prices? Is she deprived of wearing the right styles?

FRED: You take a woman who has five children and a husband; she can spend a dime on a newspaper, scan through it, and see what designs would be most attractive for her.

VIRGINIA: But how does she know which designs would be most attractive when she is analyzing herself?

FRED: She must analyze her position in her neighborhood and her own economy. She can't just pick anything without doing this analysis; it would be impossible.

VIRGINIA: In other words, you really do feel that a woman's way of life is indicated by her hair?

FRED: Yes.

VIRGINIA: By that I mean her social status, her husband's earning power, and her occupation.

FRED: Yes.

VIRGINIA: Isn't a woman with individual tastes who can project herself always outstanding? When should a woman restrict her imaginative image to the limitations of social status?

FRED: Projecting herself in this imaginative way is fine, but she also has to have the personality to carry it off. Otherwise she will be rejected.

VIRGINIA: I know a wife at an Army post. All the women

looked alike and then this woman emerged with a bun, a comb, and a red rose, and she was like an oasis in the desert. I was happy to see her. Wouldn't a woman who is individual enough in her community be able to carry it off?

FRED: That depends entirely on her strength of character.

VIRGINIA: So if a woman really wants to do it, it takes self-assurance.

FRED: Right.

VIRGINIA: Now, let's get back to your clients. Fred, are they of the theater or society?

FRED: They are fashionable women.

VIRGINIA: By that do you mean "money" women?

FRED: No.

VIRGINIA: My impression of fashionable women, many of them, has been one of complete oversimplification, almost a chaste look.

FRED: Well, that's true.

VIRGINIA: What do you think of the total look? What does "the look" mean to you, Fred?

FRED: The look is a coordinated simplification where no one particular thing stands out but the entirety is beautiful.

VIRGINIA: In other words, anyone who is "far out" cannot be fashionable?

FRED: No, I didn't say that. What I am saying is that when you coordinate the entire look, you see it as a whole.

VIRGINIA: In other words, you shouldn't be able to notice the hair?

FRED: Everything should be coordinated so that the look is a total look. Going back to our discussion about designers, there is one thing that I believe. In design of any kind, it takes a twenty-year cycle to create a fine designer.

VIRGINIA: What do you mean by that?

FRED: You can understand the cycles and eras of design only through experience. It is true that some young designers can become powerful enough to create looks but usually these are fads and only after the experience of a cycle can one become a great designer, if he holds out.

VIRGINIA: I don't understand what you mean by a twenty-year cycle.

FRED: A complete cycle happens in the fashion industry approximately every twenty years.

VIRGINIA: You mean a really drastic change?

FRED: Yes.

VIRGINIA: What do you think is the basic contributing factor to style change?

FRED: The economy of the country. When the money goes up, the hemlines go up.

VIRGINIA: I disagree. Short skirts have generally indicated a shortage of material, usually just before or during a war. But to go on to something else. How much should the color of hair influence design?

FRED: A great deal. This is another point which I take into consideration when I analyze my clients.

VIRGINIA: In other words, Fred, when you see a woman with colored hair, you ask yourself why she colored her hair. This influences you in your styling.

FRED: Most definitely.

VIRGINIA: Is there an age limit in hair color for a woman? In other words, if a woman has been blond for many years, as time passes should she change the color of her hair?

FRED: Well, to start with, unless you are born blond, the natural processes of the body coordinate the natural hair color with the skin tone and hair would normally go lighter with age to soften the face. Women with color on their hair should practice within the tone area of their age process. However, a blond can stay a blond no matter how old she gets.

VIRGINIA: Many women feel they should cover the gray and darken the hair to conceal the passing years. Do you approve of this?

FRED: Often the clients do not project their hair color with their age. If they are getting gray they should lighten rather than darken the hair. Very seldom does the body make a mistake in the color of the hair with the skin tones.

VIRGINIA: In other words you think nature is always right?

FRED: Most generally. My attitude is that a woman who changes her hair color changes her personality. I believe that nature very rarely makes a mistake in the hair tones it creates for each individual human being. When one dyes one should dye the tone, never the base color. It has always been my knowledge that brownettes and brunettes and even grays who decide to go blond also decide to change their personality and need the color to help them.

VIRGINIA: What if a woman were born with brown hair and brown was not really the most becoming hair color for her?

FRED: Then you are talking about something entirely different. You are talking about a person who sees herself as another color.

VIRGINIA: Is there anything wrong with that?

FRED: No.

VIRGINIA: When you talk about color, you are not talking about the bottle. You are talking about what changes in personality the client wants. What does that client want to be?

108

What personality does she want to choose other than her own? What is there about hers that she doesn't like?

FRED: That's why I said to you that you are not designing the hair, you are designing the mind.

VIRGINIA: If the client wanted to be blond and you looked at her and felt that this was wrong for her, is it your right to dissuade her or give her what she wants?

FRED: If she wants it, she will carry it.

VIRGINIA: In other words, a woman with atrocious taste, and there are many, might buy a beautiful, expensive dress and look atrocious in it?

FRED: I am a beautician, not a psychiatrist.

VIRGINIA: I think you are being unduly modest. I think there is a tremendous amount of psychology, not psychiatry, involved in selling women all phases of fashion. I think a woman takes more advice and criticism about fashion from her beautician than she does from her husband and best friend—which leads me to this question. Do you think a woman should consult her husband before she makes a style change and color change in hair?

FRED: Absolutely, if she is a happily married woman. My designs always take into consideration the position of the client as a reflection of her husband's position. Through conversation and observation I can usually tell how to please the husband through the strengths of the woman. That is, if she chooses to please him. Speaking of husbands of clients reminds me of a bobby-pin advertisement I once did. Four beautiful models in full makeup and my hair styles were sitting for portraits to be used in a national brochure. The client was drooling watching these lovely ladies, but when approached as to his opinion, his remark was: "Well, my wife would never wear that."

VIRGINIA: I don't agree with you. I don't think women reject beauty. In my travels all over America, I have met women in their early thirties whose hair had started to gray, not a flattering silver gray but a distinctly unflattering color that robbed the hair of its vitality, the skin of its color, and the eyes of their luster. I have said to them, "My dear, you would be so beautiful if you would restore your natural color to your hair," and eight out of ten have said to me, "My husband would never allow it." Now what about the future?

FRED: As far as the distant future is concerned, I am sure that scientists will find the solution to the problems of space travel, including the recession of hair growth. Tomorrow's woman on the moon may be lucky if she has *any* hair. I am sure the distant future will see an era of bald men and women. After all, hair merely serves as a protective covering for the brain against extremes of heat and cold. All this in spite of the fact that we use it mostly for adornment!

As I left Mr. Fredrick, I recalled something I had read recently. Research scientists have been injecting vitamins into rats and mice which have turned their hair from dark brown to pure white, and also reversed this process. I never did find out if the little fellows lived or died, but we should prepare ourselves for this sort of thing. So, in the future, you can expect to *drink your color*.

15

Diet Is Such a Bore

I think this whole world has become so diet-conscious that we've eliminated from our daily lives hospitality and graciousness and a sense of welcome to each other. There is such a guilty feeling among us, we all apologize when we enjoy food. "I never eat dessert during the week —only when I go out." How many times have you heard that? There's always an explanation. There's no more sitting down and saying, "What a fabulous pie crust! What delicious rolls!"

In our home, when we have company we have a company menu. We have potatoes, hot bread, a homemade dessert. I must tell you in all frankness that nobody has ever refused our party dinners. People who are usually penurious about their caloric intake manage to eat very nicely when they come to see us because it is an occasion and festive. Then, after they've eaten so extensively that their girdles are slightly turned over from the extra pressure, they look at me as if I were a typhoid carrier and say, "Do you eat like this all the time?"

Of course most of us have to watch our weight if we want to look trim.

I was having a late lunch recently at about three o'clock in the afternoon. The waitress had just brought me hot toasted cheese bread with a big slice of Virginia ham and melted cheddar cheese, paprika, and fresh ground pepper. The fragrance of the cheese was tickling my nostrils and my mouth was all set to enjoy this delight, when a face appeared right in front of my open mouth. It was a fan, who scolded, "Oh, you're always talking about dieting. How can you eat anything like that?"

Well, of course she ruined the whole thing for me. I mean, I enjoyed it, but only half. That's what I'm so tired of. We hear so much about dieting and dying that I don't see how we can enjoy living. They tell us that everything we're doing is killing us. I don't really see how our ancestors survived. I'm sure they died more from infection than from overweight. But I'm not sure how it is working with us. True, pressures and tensions are killing off people faster than what they eat. Yet I know a woman who's found out that water is fattening and won't touch the stuff. This doesn't surprise me, because my mother was the kind of woman who preferred that you use a profanity rather than the word "fudge." My brother and I were given dessert so seldom that we became "sweet-coholics." We couldn't wait until Mama was away to sneak candy into the house.

Diet Is Such a Bore

I know there are times when I've eaten too much and should have been more careful. But I also realize that food can take the place of some things that could be far more harmful. I've never taken a sleeping pill in my life. I don't live on tranquilizers. But I do enjoy good food. I love it. I face the fact that I will never be skinny. I watch myself because I know I have the potential for becoming very very fat, and I would not like that to happen. I've lost weight recently. Buddy Hackett said that he met 190 pounds walking down the street with a head of its own. It was what he had lost. But people who have a weight problem will always lose and gain. It seems to be a condition of their lives. Sometimes crash diets are the only way they can accomplish what they have to. Weddings are the greatest incentives I know for losing weight.

But when you are dieting, do not say to the waitress in a loud and distressed voice, "Oh, no, I never eat potatoes or bread." Just quietly skip what is passed with no apologies. Or if you are a guest in someone's home, take a very little of everything on your plate. I would rather be guilty of wasting than insulting.

"Why do you have hors d'oeuvres?" my friends all ask. "They kill the appetite." I hate such a comment, especially from those who risk china-poisoning from licking the plate. There need be no food discussion during an evening's gaiety. Dieting is as personal as your religion or your politics.

People have asked me whether I think that generosity of food goes with a generous nature. I can't help but believe that the person who is abundant with food and hospitality would be abundant with understanding and generosity. There are some people who say food is of no interest to them. I don't believe it, because why do they eat so much when they come to your house? They're trying to make excuses for their selfishness, indifference, and laziness. I know loads of people who love to accept invitations to other people's homes, and eat everything. But you never get invitations from them, or they tell you they're not entertaining because they're on a diet. This lack of reciprocity is very revealing—and I don't like what I see. I think that many food habits are ancestral and ethnic, and in the hotter climates the natives are more generous. So let's hope for a long, hot summer. There have been too many people who are too cold—maybe they'll thaw out.

But still I can't help being angry that some people—and they're invariably the skinniest you know—can push their potatoes in with a piece of bread dipped in gravy, use the whipped cream to hold the double chocolate icing on top of the shortcake, and yet never gain weight. I see these people, and I could kill them. I gain weight from looking at a Duncan Hines commercial.

I would suggest that you don't go out to lunch with a person like that. Her metabolism is different from yours. From anger at the fact that she can get away with all the calories in sight, you might be tempted to match her down the line from lasagna to pie a la mode. Such a spirit of "I'll show you" is foolhardy. You have to be honest with yourself. You have to accept your limitations.

With this warning I go back to my basic belief that far worse than a little unfashionable padding on your bones is the type of self-denial that is dehydrating and destructive. It makes you tense and tight-lipped and ungenerous. It leads to a meanness of spirit that is the absolute opposite of everything that is beautiful. I think people who like the good things of life are able to give the good things to other people.

JEAN: I met a woman some years ago about as skinny as a

114

piece of modern sculpture. And just about as hospitable. I remember a dinner party at her home. She served lobsters buffet style from a huge pile on the dining room table. It was all very informal and her guests were having a marvelous time tearing away at their lobsters. But the hostess couldn't stand the sight of all that disorder. She went around to her guests saying, "Let me take that shell away from you."

You'd say, "Oh, no, I haven't started that part yet."

She'd reply, "But it's in your way. It's so messy. Let me take it." And she walked around the room snatching all the uneaten lobster from our plates. We were so hungry, we went right from that party to a diner.

VIRGINIA: I'm not going to tell you how to diet. If you want to lose a serious amount of weight—I would say more than fifteen pounds—I think you should see your physician and get his advice on the best diet for you. There are a number of new theories about diet that involve a precise balancing of carbohydrates and fats combined with limitation of calories. I would be practicing medicine without a license if I were to prescribe a diet for you.

If your objective is to take off five or ten pounds, stop kidding—you know how to do it. You cut back on general intake, you reduce desserts to zero, you avoid gravies and sauces, and you don't skimp all day and then raid the refrigerator at night. You might fast for a day—no food, only water, black coffee, or tea. But don't prolong a fast without your doctor's consent. Don't pin your hopes on fad diets. Most of them are invented to sell magazines.

JEAN: That's right. If a magazine doesn't have a story about Jackie Kennedy to headline on its cover, the only way to sell out an issue at the newsstand is to run a big banner about a sensational new diet. The brand-new diet, as often as not, is a hodge-podge of the last six new diets concocted by a junior editor recently out of Vassar who weighs a hundred and eighty-five pounds.

VIRGINIA: I know it's not cricket to write a beauty book without discussing exercise. I will agree with the experts that body exercise is valuable. I only wish I could do more of it. Those of you who live in areas where there are exercise programs on TV have a fantastic opportunity. The most highly trained people are available right in your living room to guide you and instruct you. But if you can't follow a TV exercise program, I don't think you should worry too much about exercise if you are leading a busy life. If you're home with young children, you're bending and stretching a million times a day. Just put a little extra zing into those stretches when you reach down to retrieve a rattle or a toy. Feel the pull on your muscles. Bend down an extra time or two for good measure. Deliberately reach over to the far side of the bed when you're smoothing a sheet. Go down in a deep knee bend when you're looking for your slippers on the floor of the closet. You don't have to do your exercises on a special quilted mat with a gymnast shouting commands. Your daily life is full of opportunities to exercise.

Nora Kovach, a beautiful young ballet dancer trained in Hungary, feels that body movements made to music are more meaningful in terms of grace and relaxation than the same movements made in a gym in response to abrupt commands. "To get real looseness of your body when you exercise," she told me on a "Girl Talk" program, "do it to music. Put a record on the phonograph, preferably ballet music, but it doesn't really matter as long as the music has a gentle, smooth rhythm, and then do your exercises. If the music is from *Swan Lake,*

116

you will feel yourself before long trying to move like a swan."

I liked that *Swan Lake* suggestion a lot because I really got shortchanged in the neck department. Now every time I hear a schmaltzy tune, I wriggle my neck rhythmically. I haven't turned swanlike yet, but just being aware of my neck makes me carry it straighter and taller, and when I pass a mirror with my head held high, I realize that my neck is not so deficient after all.

Once more the marvelous lesson: If you want beauty badly enough, you will have it.

16

The Last Resorts

I've always been interested in spas, which I consider to be postgraduate milk farms. I remember that when I was at a girls' boarding school the mother of a friend of mine who had had financial reverses and had to make a living opened a milk farm. Being naïve and uninformed, I thought my friend's mother was running a kind of dairy. Later I found it was a place where tired, harassed women went to take off their girdles, to scratch the indentations left by too tight rubber, to sit out in the sun and be fanned and waited on, and to lie on pounding tables and get massaged. Incidentally, they also ate milk products. Its charm, I quickly realized, grew out of the fact that a milk farm offered a moment when a woman could think of nothing but herself. My friend's mother did very well financially, although she really solved her problem by marrying a wealthy dairy man. You might say she got right to the source.

The spa today is something of a status symbol. Maine Chance in Arizona is one of the most famous and there the Elizabeth Arden people have probably reached perfection in providing an idyllic way for a woman to divorce herself completely from responsibility and to look at herself in the mirror and see what is really there. In most instances the spa is a gift for the rich. It is not easy to afford: charges run from twenty dollars a day to five hundred dollars a week, and even higher at the posh places. Yet today there are many middle class families that can manage an occasional weekend trip to a spa without bankruptcy. We recently interviewed on "Girl Talk" a visitor from the Alps of the Catskills who runs a milk farm. She told us that she has great problems because her farm is co-ed. I don't know whether they use two doors or whether she has a separate acre for men—God's little acre was divided, you see. Her trouble was not so much sex as the need to frisk the luggage of new arrivals. Some resorts have the problem of alcoholics. At milk farms the difficulty is "corned beef-oholics." Women would come in with a brisket of beef and a bottle of brandy and they had to smell the luggage to find out who the offenders were.

I've always noticed that there's one particular muscle that women develop at milk farms. They all play cards, of course, and the shuffling of the cards is just great for the arms. But I do seriously think that if you are the type who has tremendous tensions, a demanding routine, and heavy responsibilities, it is a marvelous idea to get away for a few days. I can tell you that when you arrive and check in the doctor gives you a physical checkup. He has to make sure you're in shape for all the pampering. Then they put you on a diet and start purging you of all the poisons of having lived with your husband and children all those dreary years. They also put you on a regimen of exercise. Now I've already told you what I think of exercise and hiking and that's the main reason I haven't become a true addict of milk farms. When I see them coming at me with the gym suit or that modern dance leotard, I suddenly remember I have a fashion show to do in Peoria and I do my hiking to the nearest railroad station or airport.

The routine is really quite fantastic. Right at the outset you are stripped of any wealth symbols in which you normally wrap yourself because your clothes are taken away and you get into a uniform. (At some places, they give you back your jewels and clothes at night.) Once you're all dressed alike, you see that other people bulge at the same places you do. You find out that their hidden charms are in their arms, or other areas that were so beautifully concealed. You suddenly realize to what extent you have gotten out of shape, and this sharp realization puts you on the road back. You plunge into the massages, the heat cabinets, the hydrotherapy, the swimming—indoors and out, depending on the season—golf, tennis, ballet dancing, sometimes fencing, even, at some establishments, voice lessons for the discipline of correct breathing.

You move from sauna to whirlpool, from sweatsuit to leotard, from massage table to exercise mat, and all they feed you is a spot of tea or fruit juice or a vitamin concoction and a wild orgy of five hundred calories for dinner. At some places they work on your skin with infrared steamers and high frequency gadgets that strip away blackheads; then they apply heat packs and bombard you with ozone machines to scare away the facial impurities.

At night they try to improve your mind with lectures on current events or the stock market. Some women practice the new dance steps with each other (shades of boarding school!). Some never look up from their card tables. A few wander around, forlornly rattling their diamonds.

While I always notice the funny side of a spa, I do believe these places give you a marvelous chance to get away from men (temporarily), to look at other women, and to look at yourself. And I must confess that I adore the luxurious body lotions they soak into the skin, the fragrances they slather on, the deep, velvety towels they wrap you in when they practically carry you like a baby from massage table to perfumed tub.

Men, I am told by experts, are much more rigid than women about adhering to spa rules. They don't cheat on their diet, they wait for dinner, and they almost never smuggle food. This, I think, proves my view that overeating among women is neurotic—so much psyche is involved in all that piling up of calories.

I am sure that there are many people who would label you selfish for seizing the opportunity to get away and concentrate on your own needs. But I don't agree with them. I see it as an opportunity for you to really get to know yourself again. If you view a visit to a spa as a learning experience, perhaps you can afford it after all. And no matter which one you patronize, you're bound to hear that most sturdy of health-farm jokes, "I've lost over a hundred pounds this year, but the trouble is, it's always the same five pounds."

121

17

Tongue in Chic

For a long time I avidly read the fashion pages of newspapers and magazines, but now I thoroughly resent them. Everything seems to be aimed at the girls between eighteen and twenty-five. It is ridiculous for the whims of the young group so busy finding itself to dictate to those who have already gone through the hard knocks of experience. I don't think fashion should be a denial of youth, but neither should it be a rejection of the geriatric type of thirty.

Eugenia Sheppard, the fashion columnist, has a helpful

point of view. She believes that fashion is now operating on the two-track system. One track is made up of the kicky tricky stuff for the young crowd; the other is fashion as we've known it in the past, designed for beauty and flattery. The cutoff point for the go-go look, she feels, should be about thirty. Girls under thirty can get away with the gadgets of the moment, whether they are swingy skirts no bigger than guest towels, stringy tank tops, vinyl wrappings, or something altogether different. That is, if they're the type for such goings-on.

Those past thirty, however, should not heed the siren songs from the guitar-and-folk-rock crowd. Beautiful, wearable clothes are being designed, made, and sold every day in stores throughout the country. The trick is to find them. With half our population now under twenty-five, and all the money in the world slipping through the fast-spending fingers of the teen-agers and young twenties, it's not surprising that canny merchants woo the hipsters. What they do and wear makes news. At this moment in history they create excitement. They give a store the roar of success. The woman who wants a handsomely constructed, carefully detailed suit in larkspur blue, size fourteen, with blouse and hat to match, has to grope her way into a back department. But if she's persistent, she'll find what she wants.

I am reminded of the perfectly marvelous English woman who appeared with me in the play, *Late Love,* in summer theater. Her name is Velma Royton. She's reached her three score years and more, but she's so agile and excited about living that she's ageless. She told me one day, "I'm looking for a middle dress." I asked her what she meant by a middle dress, I thought maybe she meant middle class. "No," she said, "I'm looking for a dress with a middle, something simple with a

123

belt." She'd looked everywhere and couldn't find it. "I guess I'll have to wait until the fashion comes back," she said.

It is a pity of course that fashion in pursuing the youthful moneymakers doesn't realize that this eighteen to twenty age group changes its taste at twenty and probably again at twenty-two and is in such a state of flux that it couldn't— or shouldn't—dictate fashion to the rest of the world. There is no stability to youth. Youth is trying to find itself. I am constantly reminded of the story of the boy who turned to his father on his twenty-first birthday and asked, "Dad, how did you ever learn so much in the last three years?"

I know today when you read a fashion magazine or walk into a store, it's hard to believe that non-kooky clothes exist. For proof I suggest you turn to the society page of your local paper. The ladies on the committees for the balls and benefits, the debutantes who come out, the mothers of the brides— they can't *all* be wearing outfits left over from last year and the year before. They don't *all* have little dressmakers. They buy their charming suits, their becoming dresses, their lavish evening gowns, right where they've always bought them— from local stores or on occasional trips to bigger cities. Don't hesitate to make your fashion needs known to your local store. If there's nothing in the adult department but bell-bottom pants and dimity smocks with appliqued teddy bears —squawk! Make loud, indignant noises. Make the buyer or the merchant see the error of his ways. He'll come to his senses quickly enough.

I know it takes courage for a woman to say no to a style— "this is wrong for me." Especially when everybody's wearing it. Yet it's funny the way fashion evolution works. The original sack was a horror. But from it derived the shift, which is cut with enough shape to be wearable by most women. And from the shift has come the marvelous easy look in suits that gives a woman enormous assurance, because if she does have the battle of the bulge, the loose look hides a multitude of figure imperfections.

Knees are something else again. I think they are a part of the human anatomy that never quite got finished. Why any woman in her right mind would want to show her knees is something I'll never understand. When I first glance through the magazines with those sawed-off dresses, all I can think is that every woman looks like two Khrushchevs.

I am a size sixteen with a size fourteen hip. I am five feet eight without heels. My problem is one of minimizing the bust, achieving a long neck look. I have found by long experience that no one can design for me as well as a woman. Matthews of California, Pauline Trigere, Jo Copeland—the minute I put on something designed by one of these gifted women, I feel right. It is interesting that they are all tall women with bosoms, and I suppose they cannot help but subconsciously design for themselves. Emme designs my hats, and I am sure it is her woman's touch that makes them so wonderful.

I'm not a psychiatrist, so I can't tell you whether the male designer of dubious sex is deliberately trying to disfigure all women, or whether it's simply that he hates his mother. Obviously the well-rounded, motherly figure is repugnant to him, so he exercises his talents on behalf of the boyish-chested, flat-tummied, no buttocks woman. Now the unfortunate thing is that this boyish girl of his dreams is also the cameraman's real dream girl. The TV camera and the still camera both add a good ten pounds to a woman's figure. A photographic model must be bone skinny in order not to look pudgy.

125

Then there's another factor. When a picture is taken, the full attention must be on the garment. If the girl herself is at a minimum, you notice all the detail of the outfit and are not distracted by her contours. That's why the typical *Vogue* or *Harper's Bazaar* model looks like a skeleton with a few veins on it whose life has to be short because she can't survive for long on that diet. She's got to start eating again.

Women have asked me what to do about the dress that just doesn't work. It seemed like an awfully good idea in the shop, but once it's worn, it's clearly a mistake. We all make such mistakes, and I think it's better to wear last year's dress than to wear a mistake just because we've made it. Sometimes if you let a mistake hang in your closet for a little while you can come back to it with a fresh eye and find it more acceptable. If you are handy, perhaps you can redrape or retrim it in some way. But if time makes it worse rather than better—well, you'll just have to give it to Cousin Josephine and hope she's happier in it than you.

Have you ever noticed that it's often the women who shop the most fiercely who make the worst errors? The people who have to drive a hard bargain, who *have* to look in every store, and have to try on *everything*—they're the ones who get the alligator shoes with the mismarkings, the bag with the flaw in it. I think if you see a beautiful and becoming summer dress on sale in the winter or in a cruise line, you should buy it then. I don't think you should worry if your purchase is out of season. The time you *should* worry is when you are not mad about your purchase in the store. You're not going to like it any better when you get home. In fact, you're not going to like it at all when you get home.

I should add here that I don't believe a woman should take anyone else along when she shops. I can't bear to shop with someone else for two reasons: One, if a dress doesn't fit and has to be let out, I wouldn't let my best friend know; and two, I think you get more attention from the salesperson when you're alone. Of course I'm assuming you have some idea of what you want when you go shopping. You've glanced at the fashion magazines, you've seen the advertisements in your local newspapers, you know the purpose for which you want the new dress or coat. If your mind is a complete blank, you have no idea of what you want and why, and you spend several hours trying on everything in sight without any serious intention of buying, you are depriving a working person of her livelihood, and this is a very dishonest thing to do.

You have the right to take as long as you want in order to make a careful and thoughtful choice. But you do not have the right to do your basic homework on a salesperson's time. What's more, this type of indecision means you don't know yourself, you don't know your colors, your needs, and you may as well learn right now that nothing is a bargain if it isn't becoming and you can't use it.

I don't think there's anybody rich enough to afford cheap dresses, and especially cheap suits. By cheap I do not necessarily mean low priced—there are many wonderful things these days priced at a very modest level. I mean cheap workmanship, shoddy material, indifferent construction. If you're buying at a budget price-level, you have to be all the more alert for poor quality. And if you've never owned something really good, may I suggest that the next time you're thinking of buying a suit, you put the money in the bank instead and wait until the following season, or the next year, when you would normally be buying another suit. Take twice the money you would ordinarily spend, shop carefully, and you will have the pleasure of owning a garment that will more than repay your investment. I have suits that are at least eight years old. At a recent movie opening I wore a gorgeous gold brocade coat that I've had for six years and loved all that time.

Keep away from overjazzy styling. When the adornment is part of the dress or suit, people remember it and get tired of it. Let the adornment be in your jewelry or accessories and the dress will look new far longer. There are so many fabulous devices now to change the look of a dress; with a touch of color, a scarf, a bit of fur, a good, simple dress can lead a dozen lives. You know that I appear on "Girl Talk" five days a week, but you may not know that I furnish my own wardrobe. Each dress I buy has to appear four or five or six times a season, yet look new and fresh. One of my favorite tricks is to buy a dress with a very plain neckline and have a variety of over-the-head silk or chiffon scarves in prints, florals, and geometric designs, to shape as I please at the throat. So my advice to you is to buy a simple dress with good body lines, easy fit, lovely color, and fine fabric.

The main thing I have noticed about women at the many luncheons I attend is that they are overdressed. I do not believe that anywhere in the world do you wear a print satin dress with sequins to a luncheon. Yet I've seen exactly such horrors sitting down to the chicken patties. With flowered hats, too. The woman who truly stands out at any luncheon is understated. She wears a simple suit and a hat that isn't part of the botanical gardens. Her jewelry, whether real or costume, is never overwhelming. I think the overflowered hat or the overpowering anything should be avoided.

128

I've noticed something else. As the luncheon gets more costly, the clothes become simpler. At a $100-a-plate charity luncheon, for example, as compared to a $10-a-plate event, the jewelry is simpler, the hair styles are simpler, the fashions are simpler. So if fashion is an indication of financial level, the bitter joke is on the woman who, by overdecking herself, advertises her insecurity.

I am reminded of something amusing that happened on a recent trip to Cleveland. The hotel maid who was helping me zip up the back of my dress said, "I know what you are—you're a remodel."

"I guess I do need remodeling," I told her.

"I knew it," she answered, "the minute I saw you. What store do you remodel in?"

She's right, because I do remodel every year, and we all can remodel. Weight doesn't necessarily change, but measurements often do. I put on a dress the other day that Harry hated the two or three times I wore it last year. This year he said, "That dress looks great on you." He was right. It hung in an entirely different way.

Well, partly it hung in a different way and partly his eye had become used to the loose-fitting look of that particular dress. That's something we all have to recognize—the gradual education of our eyes. When we saw our first abstract paintings some years back, we were baffled and wondered what was going on. Now we're surprised if a painting has a house or a face in it that we can recognize. The giant floral prints that are accepted today looked gaudy and unwearable a season or two back.

JEAN: I know a perfect example. When boots first came out, I swore I'd never walk around looking like a Cossack. Now I can't imagine getting through a winter without a couple of pairs of warm, smart boots.

VIRGINIA: The time lag in acceptance also applies to a new makeup or a new hair style. A woman is apt to be instantly defeated if her family, not used to the new look, greets the change with groans and complaints. A woman needs a good deal of courage to stand up to that sort of criticism. But if she knows in her heart that the new style or the new color is right for her, and she has the backing of a salesgirl or a beautician whose judgment she trusts, I think she will somehow find that courage.

JEAN: What about the times when the criticism is justified? Isn't it possible that a woman may be oversold on something new, or may have temporarily lost her reason and come home in a completely grotesque getup?

VIRGINIA: I don't think she's lost her reason; I think she's found her reason. She may have found the wrong expression for it, but she found a reason within herself to want to change. I think this brings up a very important point. People are often trying to mask what they really are. They use makeup or a fashion look as a mask to hide what they are, so they can look out and watch the world from behind a facade which they created but which is not their real identity. Hair color and dress color represent a need within you, a need to be lovely, a need to be appreciated, a need to be wanted. When I hear from women that their husbands don't notice from one year to the next what they're wearing, I think I'd want to investigate why John didn't notice—especially if he didn't notice something as assertive as a red hat with purple ostrich feathers. I'd try to find out in what way visual contact has been lost. Such lack of notice is beyond the retina of the eye. It is psychological.

JEAN: But aren't there men who are completely oblivious and never notice?

VIRGINIA: They have to be reminded. You have to make them aware of the fact that you adore them, that you want them to be proud of you. Your husband has to know that people are judging him by the way you look. I insist that if your husband doesn't notice you there's a reason for it. What's more, other people do notice you, and many of them wonder about *him*.

I do think, though, that fashion needs a boost every so often, a new charge of energy. I used to be furious with Vidal Sassoon for those chopped-off haircuts. But soon I realized that he's done more for the beauty business than anyone of his time because those who were wise adapted his hair styles and relearned the art of cutting. Women found the results beautiful, chic, and charming.

I suspect that fashion works the same way. I used to hate the idea of women in slacks. I carried on a one-woman crusade against slacks. You should have heard me. But today when I visit my grandchildren or take them to the park, what do you think I wear? Slacks. What else could I possibly wear? It just happens that I am flat in the places where a girl should be flat in back so that I can wear slacks quite well and some people think I look better in them than I do in dresses. But I always try to wear a little jacket or coat over the slacks. I wear a simple top and simple shoes. And when I get on the floor to play with the children, I am so comfortable and so much at ease that I have a great deal more fun and so do they.

I think we are about to see a change in fashion. I don't know what it is going to be, but I'd like to take a look into my crystal ball. I think our future cosmetically is going to have bright, vivid lips and bright, vivid nail polish. We are going back to a whole brighter point of view. I think we need it. We are overimmersed in pastel thinking. Our politics are pastel. In too many areas we are passive where we should be active.

Fashionwise, I think that dresses are going back to fifteen inches from the ground. The full skirt is coming back because knees have been too much with us. We are going to return to soft fabrics as opposed to the heavy, almost upholstery-type fabrics and vinyls we've used. I can see a return to the cuddly woman instead of the capable woman. Women are going to be more cuddly than capable. What do you think, Jean? What's your prophecy?

JEAN: I don't see any really drastic changes ahead in terms of crinolines or bustles. The current loose, easy look is right for the busy lives most women live. We'll have swings back and forth within a fairly narrow range, but I suspect the shift is never going out completely—it's too easy and comfortable. We'll move the emphasis from one part of the anatomy to another and uncover different areas at different times. The knee, I hope, has about had it—it's a pretty boring piece of anatomy. One of the troubles is that there are not enough parts of the human body to exploit, to reveal or to conceal.

VIRGINIA: Well, Jean, if you think anything has been concealed, just go to the beach.

18

It's Good to Be in the Red

One of the great excitements of our time is the resurgence of color, not only in cosmetics, but also in clothes. Not since the days of the splendid courts of Europe have we seen such beautiful, luscious pastels, such ringing jewel tones, such richness of coloring everywhere. The women of the court were compelled to be beautiful; to provide delight to the eye was a service they rendered to their government as ladies-in-waiting and royal attendants. But when America emerged as a nation, no longer was color an acquittal, it was a guilt. The Puritan influence, the Quaker influence, the lack

133

of luxury fabrics in the new colonies, brought grays and browns and blacks to the fore. Self-concern became equated with vanity, which in turn was a sin.

We have to skip down history to the arrival of Jacqueline Kennedy at the White House to find a revival of the beauty of color. With excitement and extravagance she reintroduced us. But this time, thanks to economic opportunity and technological advances, color was no longer limited to the ladies of privilege. Mrs. Kennedy's basic shifts in oatmeal color and emerald green and soft jade and pink became instantly available to everyone. Color has begun to run wild in all our lives, and I couldn't be happier.

I wish women could realize why they have for so long retreated to the security of black. I can understand that if her figure is heavy, a woman finds black marvelous for definition purposes. But take a nice-looking woman with a good figure. Why does she venture out Saturday night after Saturday night in old, faithful black? And with that same monotonous string of pearls, too? Doesn't she see that her chief concern is safety? She is running for cover. She doesn't want to be talked about. She's scared she may be noticed.

Every year they come out with black and they say, "Black is new. The new color is black. It's exciting!" You wonder what can be exciting about it. I find that as I get older and as I get blonder, and I seem to be getting blonder as I'm getting older, I need the light of color around my face more than ever. That's why some women who suddenly become platinum blonds are beautiful for the first time in their lives. They discover color.

Black shouldn't be a sanctuary. It shouldn't be something to hide in. You should not wear black and a string of pearls

134

because someone else does—even if that someone else is the social leader in your community. Women who head charity drives and hold high office in civic affairs might be very much worth emulating in terms of behavior. But they don't necessarily set dress standards. And you don't have to wear black simply because Madam Chairman does. And even if you wear black, your dress and your neckline may not call for pearls at all. Or maybe you're the type, like many of my guests on "Girl Talk," who wears ropes of pearls and a pin holding them at the neck, dangling earrings, and bracelets all the way up the arm, and still doesn't look one bit overdressed.

The point is to know what *you* can wear and not to allow magazine articles or your insecure friends to limit you to styles and colors that are not right for you. Naturally you're going to be influenced to some extent by those around you, and especially by those with strong personalities. This brings up a very interesting question, because we are all susceptible to people around us as far as personality is concerned.

For example, I think I have a very definite personality—the kind that makes itself felt. Someone asked me how I got it. I said that from the time I was a child I sat back and I watched the most popular woman in the room. I started with the girls in class. I loved watching my mother's friends who came to play bridge, or attending meetings she held of groups to help the blind. I tried to figure out which woman brought the most excitement into the room when she entered it. What was it— a fragrance she wore? A bunch of violets pinned on her coat? I remember a marvelous blond woman who came in wearing a dove-gray suit with a krimmer stand-up collar and a krimmer Cossack hat, and pinned at the neck were fresh Parma violets.

Time and again I realized it was color that focused attention on an exciting personality. Does it really matter if it's the other way around—that the exciting personality chose to enhance her own outstanding qualities through the use of color? While I was still quite young, I became aware that even if you do not have the personality to make people notice you, or are not *aware* that you have the personality, you can wrap yourself in color and fool the world into thinking you're a peacock instead of a mouse. Color becomes an incentive to change yourself. You owe it to other people who have to look at you.

I once walked into a room in a marvelous coral-color suit, a shrimpy-coral color, and someone said, "You brightened my whole day with that color." I remember a girl who came to see me in an oatmeal-color outfit with tangerine jewelry. I said, "Oh, you look so stunning. Don't you adore that color combination?"

She said, "I don't know—I don't feel strongly about it, but everyone says they like it, so that makes me feel good."

An example very much to the point is Ann Pinchot, an editor friend. She is a dignified, stately woman, but I never realized how pretty she is until the other day, when she arrived in a delphinium blue knit dress and over it a checked coat in white and the same delphinium blue, and a most becoming little white hat. I said to myself at that moment, "Ann is a very pretty woman."

I think it was Joseph Cotten's wife, Patricia Medina, who saw in a shop in London a fantastic prayer blanket from one of the Arab countries. It was red, green, orange, purple, and gold. It was incredible. She bought the blanket and had it made into the most fantastic coat you ever saw. This took daring and enterprise. I was especially impressed because I could see a million colorful blankets and never think of a transformation into a coat.

I remember a very sober occasion when I was to give a talk for the American Cancer Society drive, and I was wondering what sort of outfit to wear. I had at that time a very beautiful black outfit with powder blue trim. I was tempted to wear it. Then I said, No, I can't wear that because I am a cancer cure, and I want to get up in front of these people and I want them to see someone who is vital and full of life. I want to be a symbol of the new hope that is offered to those who in the past might not have lived. So I wore a raspberry wool suit. It consists of a raspberry wool skirt and jacket. Under the collar it has a raspberry satin band that crisscrosses, an inset of raspberry satin near the waistline of the jacket, and the blouse, a shell of the same satin. I got enough material from my dressmaker to have a big dome hat made of the satin, and I was lucky enough to get a cobra bag and shoes of the same raspberry. I wore pale, pale pink kid gloves and amethyst jewelry that was my grandmother's.

When I stood up to talk, all of a sudden people sat up and became attentive. Even before I said a word I captured their attention and their hopes through the brilliance of color. In my talk I told them of my tremendous heartache during my illness with cancer and the agony I went through at the time of my diagnosis. But soon the prognosis became one of hope for me, and I was given a second chance, just as many others would be if people were generous enough with their funds and their support. Someone said to me afterward, "You didn't have to say a word. Just looking at you in that incredible pink,

I knew how vibrant and alive you were and I believed in the hope you brought."

I am a blond with brown eyes and a pink tone to my skin. I find I look best in shocking pinks and blues, pale yellow, and winter white and beige. I am very bad in gray. I am fine in a cocoa brown, but not in a dark brown. I don't look well in orange, but I can wear coral. I wear all of these colors, and I always have shoes to match or contrast. I feel strongly that shoe and bag colors are an indispensable part of a complete color effect. I do not believe in all-purpose black or brown or navy accessories. I am lucky enough to be able to afford shoes and bags to match most of my outfits. If I couldn't have matching shoes and bags, I'd use a toast or a bone color and wear it all year round. I think it's important to lighten and brighten an outfit with light shoes, in calf or grained calf or a skin such as cobra or alligator.

A good trick to remember when you buy a suit or dress or a coat is to ask the salesgirl if she can get you an extra half-yard of the fabric from the manufacturer, to make a hat. Some women are skillful enough to do it themselves. Others can cover an old hat with a new fabric. Or you can get a milliner to do it for you. If this is for a really special occasion, you may want to take the hat along when you have your hair done, so that your stylist can make your coiffure compatible with your hat. Or you may do it the other way around—have your hair styled as you expect to wear it with the hat and let the hat's shape and draping follow your hair. I am very committed to hats despite their general decline in popularity, and I feel that no matter how beautifully her hair is done, a woman is not really dressed unless she is wearing a hat.

Color is the magic that causes recognition or re-recognition of your good features by your friends, and also by yourself. Color can do it for you in your home, in your clothes, in your makeup, and above all in your hair color. Color is your best friend. Be bold with it!

19

You Can Take It with You

           I cannot stand the smug attitude of the very trim, thin-ankled, nonmadeup, boyish, clipped women who go on TV programs sponsored by airline or steamship companies or luggage manufacturers to show you how marvelously you can travel with an enlarged marshmallow box and go to six countries and change costumes constantly and meet a rich man who notices you for your clothes. This is the most ridiculous concept.

But I do realize that when we travel, most of us take too much. I always work on the assumption that I'm going to take everything with me because I don't want the second wife to have anything if the plane crashes. Now I feel strongly that the big thing about packing for travel, especially if like me you make frequent trips, is organizing your closets and knowing where everything is so that the chore of finding things you want to take does not negate the whole pleasure of the trip.

Harry and I live alone in a five-room apartment with plenty of space. I have three closets for myself; one is for summer, one is for spring and fall, and the third is for winter. Since clothes are now designed for all year round, colors are no indication of the season, and whites and pastels are worn all winter, I find increasingly that the fall-spring closet and the winter closet are interchangeable. In each closet I have appropriate underwear, gloves, handkerchiefs, shoes, dresses, and coats.

Of course I can already see you laughing as you read this: "Look at her with all that space, and I'm lucky if I have a quarter of a closet and six inches of shelf room for myself. With my five children, I'm lucky if I have two dresses." But let's dream of the ideal way to manage these things and let's hope one of these days you realize your dream.

Another thing I've done is to hang double rails for men's suits, and I used to have them for Lynn's things when she was small. That's the quickest way I know to double closet space— to hang one rod somewhat higher than normal level and the other halfway down, leaving room to accommodate suits and short clothes. I wonder if you know that there are special hangers available with long poles attached, so that you can reach down suits or jackets from the upper rod with complete ease.

When I'm told by Clairol, the company for which I serve

as good will ambassador, that I have to take off instantly to appear in a store in a warm climate, I don't have to raise a cyclone to pack my bags. I go to the proper seasonal closet for a trip south. More realistically, perhaps, you go to the attic closet, if you're in a house, or the left end of the closet, if that's where you try to assemble your lightweight knits and warm-weather clothes.

Now, what do you take?

Many shops are showing you those adorable three- or four-piece outfits that get you through the entire day, from pool to evening gala. You have your shorts on, then you put on the little skirty-pie, and then you add a strapless blouse and a long-sleeved—and you know what, you look like the same person in all the pieces! I think it's ridiculous. How can you wear the same fabric and the same print for the old you on the beach in the morning, and the new you dancing in those tropical nights?

Just show me a dress you can take everywhere and wear everywhere, and I'll tell you it's a dress you can wear nowhere. It's like a fun dress. Every time a saleswoman shows me a fun dress I'm afraid I'm going to be locked up for homicide. I don't believe in the whole business of giving animate qualities to inanimate things. Fabric, color, line, should reveal you and not have a life of its own. What's more, when you switch from one type of dress to another—from sport clothes to dinner clothes—there should be a change in your makeup, your hair style. You should never be static. You change. You're animate. You're the one having fun.

So if you have very limited packing space my advice is to take only one suit and wear it every day in the daytime. But then take a different cocktail dress and a different evening dress, so that you can really feel exciting when you change clothes. Besides, if you go on the kind of trips most people do, you rarely stay in a place more than two or three days. So your clothes constantly look new. Naturally you must have every accessory to go with your outfits. You may think you're being very clever by taking black patent leather because it goes with everything. Well, it also ruins everything.

All the couture people I've talked to about coming trends in clothes put great emphasis on foot accent color, bag accent color, color, color, color! That safe brown, navy, or black shoe is not the only answer. If you don't have room to take matching accessories, carry bone or taupe.

When I asked women who are veteran travelers to share their packing tips with me, I was delighted to learn how often their views paralleled my own. Jean Baer, who drew on her experience of seventeen trips to Europe in thirteen years, and ten trips to the Caribbean, for her widely selling travel book, *Come with Me,* takes one big bag, full, and one small overnight bag, empty. For the return trip both bags are full. "And I usually weigh twenty pounds more on the return flight," she says, "not all of it food."

She takes her regular clothes, not special travel outfits; always includes a warm topcoat and suit, even in summer; finds sleeveless pastel wool dresses a great asset in any season, and no matter how tight the squeeze, includes one glamorous evening dress. On some trips she brings back the evening dress unworn, but it has well earned its space by making it possible several times for her to accept an unexpected invitation to a gala party or ball at which she would have felt dowdy in a simple cocktail sheath.

A rather sharp critic of the American woman traveler is Brit-

143

isher Peggy Scott-Duff, who was recently retained by Saks Fifth Avenue in New York to counsel customers on the go. Peggy deplores the American view that a travel wardrobe is different from a home wardrobe. She points out that a French girl traveling in Greece would wear the same sandals she wears at home and the Greeks wear in Greece. But the American wears those supersensible oxfords she's bought expressly for climbing ruins and steeples and museum stairs.

The American's suitcase is full of unchic drip-dries she wouldn't be caught wearing to an automatic laundry at home. That's because she has a totally mistaken notion that Europe has never heard of fast laundering or dry cleaning. The truth is that cleaning and laundering services are almost miraculously speedy in good hotels throughout the Continent. Peggy says an American can be spotted a block away on a European boulevard by her practical walking shoes, her shirtwaist drip-dry, and her fur which really would have been better off at home.

For her own jaunts, which have taken her almost everywhere, Peggy packs only one coat that can be worn day and night (it might be white wool), two sets of black accessories, one for day and another for evening, and a variety of scarves which she drapes over a little base she perches on the top of her head.

My only dissent from Peggy's view is in those black accessories. I would make mine bone. But I have no quarrel with the original head covering that milliner Sally Victor has created for the Jet Set. It is an oversized, reversible, eighteen-inch-square beret that ties on with a drawstring. One side is white vinyl, the other side black silk. When not on the head it can be carried by its drawstring as a handy stowaway for curlers, hair pieces, and other coiffure equipment. On the head, rain or shine, it camouflages curlers far better than a scarf because it has its own shape and does not take on the tell-tale bumps of rollers. Sally Victor recommends it particularly for air travel: Wear your curlers on the plane so that you arrive in Madrid, Tokyo, or Dallas with a fresh-from-the-hairdresser look. I guess it will have to do until airlines supply dryers—with built-in earphones, of course, to catch the soundtrack of those inflight movies.

What makeup do you take on a trip? Again, it should not be something unfamiliar that you have acquired specifically for your journey. When you're away and hurried, you need even more urgently than at home a comfortable, tried-and-true beauty routine. Buy your usual products in small sizes or repack them in plastic bottles or jars. Check on the climate of your destination. I always call ahead and make sure of what to expect. If I'm bound for freezing territory I don't pack the astringent. If I'm headed for an extremely humid place I take a hairspray with extra holding power. When I go south, in addition to suntan oil I pack a slightly darker powder than I normally use, a deeper-toned rouge, a darker and brighter lipstick, and a lighter nail polish.

A separate plastic-lined bag for makeup, personal items, and jewelry is always a good idea. It saves your good clothes from leaks and spills, and if large bags go astray you have your essentials in your hand. A few extra lipsticks or mascara wands make most welcome gifts abroad. If you run out of anything, don't panic. You will find well-known American brand names almost anywhere around the globe. But why not experiment with local products? You will be astonished to discover that continental lines sold at premium prices in fine stores here are the popular brands in Europe, priced well within your budget.

Don't hesitate to visit beauty parlors abroad. Prices are usually modest, even in posh salons. Service is often more leisurely and elegant than you are accustomed to at home. The beautician may give you a whole new perspective on yourself. Just one caution: Unless you're very daring about hair color and willing to live with some unexpected results, pack right with your passport a package of your hair color preparation, or at the very least the brand and formula number from your hairdresser.

Jane Kilbourne, fashion and travel consultant for Pan American Airways, who has clocked a total of two million miles in her own journeyings, tells women to make a list of what they think they'll need before they pack a thing. "Then," she says, "cut the list in half by eliminating all the 'just in case' items." She suggests packing the things you will need the first few days on top. Pack in layers using plastic envelopes for blouses, shirts, and underwear. Plastic envelopes are also ideal for soap, damp bathing suits, and laundry.

Materials which tend to wrinkle easily should be packed with tissue paper between each fold. Button all buttons and zip all zippers to keep garments from creasing in the wrong places. Fold dresses and jackets at the waistline and place flat in your suitcase, or pack on hangers if you have a val-pack type case. You can then scoop clothes from case to closet in one motion. Miss Kilbourne urges you to stuff shoes with socks, handkerchiefs, and other small items. Slip shoes into plastic bags. Bedroom slippers should be on top for easy access.

A small travel alarm will come in handy. Light sleepers might consider a sleeping mask and ear plugs. A few extra buttons, needle, and thread are useful. So is a roll of Scotch tape for quick mending. And if you really want to feel sophisticated, pack your curlers, rollers, and hair scarves around your wig in your wigcase. Of course you know there are women who wouldn't go anywhere without a status-enhancing wigcase. Not all these women actually own wigs. They fill the case with lunch, their knitting, or stuffed toys for the children.

Now I think I've told you how fastidious I am about always having my clothes perfectly cleaned and pressed. Harry can tell you how many times I've had my hand on the door to go out and have made the mistake of looking down at my dress. If there's a single crease anywhere, I call out to him, "Hold the elevator, I've just got to give this a touch with the iron." And the dress is over my head and on the ironing board in one minute flat.

Well, the thing that I find invaluable when I travel is steam. I mean the steam you get in the bathroom when you turn on the tub or shower as hot as it will run. Hang up your dress or coat or robe or whatever on the shower rod, close the door, and wait a few minutes until the wrinkles evaporate. Whether you're in a no-service motel, the most elegant hotel in the world, or a house guest in someone's home, put the shower on hot *and* full blast and in ten minutes you'll have an exquisitely crease-free dress.

I'm not trying to devalue the traveling iron. Of course you should have one—especially one that works on both AC and DC because you never know what you're going to find. I once blew out the electricity on an entire floor of a hotel because I plugged an iron into the wrong current. But don't forget the steaming trick. I only wish it worked as well on my face.

Now I must tell you about my one travel tragedy, which

turned out to be a comedy after all. I flew into Los Angeles some years ago and when I went to claim my bag I was given an identical suitcase which I knew at a glance wasn't mine. I carried on quite a bit, but it didn't do me any good. Whoever had my bag had already left the airport and there was nothing for me to do but take potluck with the bag that was wished on me. Well, wouldn't you know my luck—I was stuck with a pregnant woman's bag. Although it's hard to tell by today's styles, I knew she was pregnant because there was a little drawstring over the abdomen of every dress. I suppose I should be happy that she was the only woman in America whose clothes fitted me without alteration. I had a speaking engagement and simply had to wear one of her dresses. Somehow I got through the evening.

Afterward the error was straightened out. I wrote the woman a thank-you card for the use of her dress. And I did remember to send a small gift to her baby—it was a boy—born exactly one month later. Now that's what I really call a hazard of travel.

20

The Troubled Teens

When I look back at life, I think the worst years for me were my teen-age years. I know they're supposed to be glorious. But they weren't for me, and I don't think they're especially glorious for the teen-agers of today. The big city teen-agers, and they are the ones I know, so often seem to be drained, harassed, disillusioned. They have the weight of the whole world on their shoulders.

Only occasionally into our "Girl Talk" studio comes one of the marvelous young girls with sun-bleached hair, a lovely apricot-peach in the cheeks, a pale, but not white, lipstick, a

149

glistening healthy eye, a figure that has a little meat on it, with grace about her and a feeling that there is a woman inside waiting to bloom. It's as if you look at the bud and see the pink of the flower petal just waiting to burst out. She is ripe with her potential.

For a long time I very rarely saw that quality of "ripe with her potential" in teen-agers of today. In fact, I was overcome with what I can only call a sense of horror over the young teen-age group. The teen-agers I met and read about seemed to be one of America's greatest disasters. But now I take some small pride in the realization that maybe I'm not as old as I thought I was when I looked at myself in the mirror this morning, because I am able to admit that I was completely wrong about the youngsters.

Some of it's a change in the teen-agers. Some of it's a change in my eyes and the way I look at young people. But today I see long, glossy hair, as opposed to hair that once looked as if it was dressed in a mud factory. I see healthy, clean-scrubbed looks. I see a delicacy of makeup—often so delicate that what I formerly thought was the unmadeup face I now realize was a very artful achievement. I've noticed particularly the young girls on TV commercials and the ones with the youthful roles in the dramatic series—and I've come to understand that they are stunning in a certain hip style, which I used to think was kooky and ugly but now I recognize as smartly contemporary.

I think we all tend to have anxiety over anything terribly new and different—and the young people do have a new and different look about them. Now, as I have become accustomed to that look, I realize we have all been a little harsh on the youngsters. I think they are their own critics. They set up their own guidelines. They are crying for self-identification. And I think they have done a marvelous job in evolving a look and a style that is truly their own.

If you've heard me criticizing the eccentricities and way-out gimmicks of the young, you understand what a tremendous admission I am making now. It took time. My eye had to get used to a look that was so unfamiliar to me that for a long time it was frightening.

I am not famous for my patience, not at all. But I can only commend to you patience in dealing with the young. If you wait things out a bit, they change, and so do you.

But patience doesn't explain everything, including the far-out costumes of some of the young folks. Just the other day I saw walking down the street ahead of me in the Broadway area a pair of beautiful twin girls with long hair of the same color curling to their shoulders, in identical tight pants and jackets.

"My goodness," I thought to myself, "it's the Doublemint twins on their way to a commercial."

I didn't have my watch, so I went up to one of them and said, "Pardon me, dear, what time is it?" She, I mean he, turned around, and he had a goatee. I'm telling you, only their doctors know for sure.

I suppose some people attribute the long-hair look for boys to Bonnie Prince Charlie. I'm always surprised that the Queen doesn't send her son out for a haircut more often. I know perfectly well that in the past men wore long hair—but their masculinity was never in question, for with dueling and horseback riding and seducing ladies of the court, the boys were kept pretty busy.

I would have been tempted to say that the long-haired look for men was a European invention until I saw an old movie on television the other day, starring Joel McCrea, with a haircut

151

like the Beatles'. He was wearing a deerskin jacket and had a musket slung over his shoulders, and there wasn't much room for his musket, there was so much hair brushing his shoulders. I guess we've forgotten that the men of our West, the mountaineers, the Indian fighters, the most masculine of our folk heroes went around in long page-boys. Maybe there wasn't a barber shop out on the range. Or maybe we'd better do some reevaluating of our thoughts on this touchy subject of long hair.

I sometimes wonder what would happen if Lynn, my daughter, were still a teen-ager living at home, and she brought a boy in dungarees with long unwashed hair to our house. I suspect she would be locked in and the young man would be locked out. Harry would physically remove from the premises any young man who looked that way. I think it is ridiculous that parents get panic-stricken and insist they're helpless. They simply abdicate to the census taker, who tells them that 50 percent of the population is now under twenty-five. Do you know why that is? Maybe it's because the parents have all died off. Who can bear so much?

Yet it seems to me that the young girl who grows up in a home in which she is surrounded by personal cleanliness and a certain amount of good, healthy vanity on the part of her mother, will have that same vanity about herself. When a young girl grows up amid the soft, sweet smells of a woman, and the atmosphere is gentle and feminine, I don't think she's going to want to look like a waterfront tough.

The problem, obviously, is to find out what has made some young men want to look feminine and some young women eager to look masculine. And maybe this is a problem without an easy answer. James Laver, a distinguished British historian

152

of fashion who is on the staff of the Victoria and Albert Museum in London, said some very disturbing things about youth, sex, and clothing recently at a luncheon of the Fashion Group in New York. He pointed out that fashion is dictated by the deepest unconscious desire of the opposite sex. Through most of recorded history the human race has been living in a patriarchy, and during this era women have responded to men's desires by uncovering first one area of their anatomy and then another.

Today, according to Mr. Laver, we seem to be moving out of a patriarchy and into a matriarchy. This is a major shift in social organization and could logically be expected to bring enormous upheaval in fashions. Today's confusion of the he-she wardrobe merely mirrors the present confusion in male-female roles in our fast changing society.

Where does this lead? The outlook, according to Mr. Laver, is rather alarming. If we are really headed into a matriarchy, we should take note that in prehistoric matriarchies the men went about in gaudy animal skins and the ladies stayed in their caves, naked. "It is entirely possible," says the British historian, "that women of the future will have only two garments—maternity dresses and dungarees."

Well, I don't like that prospect one bit. I'm glad I won't be around for it if, unhappily, it comes true. And I'm just as glad I don't have to contend with the incredibly confusing world and shifting mores that confront our young people. I still don't like shoulder bobs for boys and garage mechanics' clothes for girls. I don't like stringy, unkempt hair, no lipstick, and raccoon eyes. I sympathize with the young people's need to try out different faces and different personalities. It's their business to experiment; I recognize that. And I suppose it's our business as adults to watch and observe them with just the right mixture of concern, disapproval, astonishment, and love.

So one thing I will say to parents of teen-agers: Keep in mind that the teen-age years are a difficult time. The youngsters are trying to find themselves. They're desperate to achieve personal identity. And we should not forget that we all underwent that same search at one time in our lives. I remember that when I was twelve years old, I bought myself a printed silk dress cut on the bias that reached all the way to my ankles. I hid the dress until the day we were going from Chicago to a family party in Racine, Wisconsin. When I came out of my room in that dress, my mother almost fainted. I should have been in a middy blouse and pleated skirt and here I was in a femme fatale gown almost to the floor. And at twelve years old, mind you. So I guess young people never make it easy for their parents. I wouldn't want to go through what my mother went through with me. I wouldn't even want to go through my own youth again. How about you, Jean?

JEAN: We're not going to have an argument about this because I completely agree with you. I so often get into discussions with friends about whether we'd want to go back and be teen-agers again. I know that I for one wouldn't. And for two very different reasons. I think the world of the young person today is much more difficult than it was for us. They don't seem to have much fun. They all have money or can get money through jobs, but that doesn't solve their problems. They're so troubled and turned in upon themselves and suffering about their identity, they've lost nearly all gaiety and sense of enjoyment. As for the second reason, I wouldn't want to give up what I've learned and what I've experienced to go back to those early groping days.

VIRGINIA: But we don't want to leave you with the impression that there's never a laugh in youth today. I am reminded of the marvelously funny thing I heard from Irene Copeland, the beauty editor of *Seventeen* magazine. She received a letter from a frantic reader who wrote, "Dear Editor: Please help me. I'm in terrible trouble. How do I keep my mascara from getting on my bangs?"

21

The World of Plastic Surgery

One of the most interesting things I've talked about with women since I've been on the air has been the cosmetic therapy known generally as plastic surgery. Until quite recently I thought of plastic surgery only in terms of having one's nose fixed. But today there is a whole world of what they call baggage removal—bags under the eyes, the tuck here, the nip there.

Most of the women I've met who have used plastic surgery are not so much interested in lying about their age as in continuing in a job or profession in which an age line is a retiring line. When I look at myself, I see now that I drag and sag where I never used to. When I'm alone I have to admit that I take my hands and I push up the lines around the mouth and under the eyes to see how I look. But I realize when I do this that I am looking at a face of the past and I don't really want to go back there. There could be so much loneliness in going back to an era all your friends have left.

I think plastic surgery is a wonderful thing for someone who does not feel lovely or for someone who has a great disfigurement that can be corrected. Jean, have you seen many of your friends who've had plastic surgery? How do you feel about it?

JEAN: Well, a friend of mine has an uncle who's a plastic surgeon, and she told me some time ago that the big thing that season was the thigh pleat. They take in the extra flesh along the inner thigh.

VIRGINIA: What do you mean—do you mean the corrugated armpit I'm always talking about, the pelican arm and thigh of a woman who's reduced a great deal without exercise?

JEAN: Yes, that's it—the sagging nonmuscle flesh on arms and legs. They just pleat it away.

VIRGINIA: It reminds me of the young woman I met recently who had just had twins and told me she had also had abdominal surgery. She had all the stretch marks removed from the abdominal area. I said, "Why? Don't you expect to have more children?" She said, "I don't know." I said, "But why did you do it? Are you a belly dancer?" She said, "No, but how else could I wear a bikini?" I think that's pretty absurd. That's the kind of vanity I don't care for at all. Jean, would you go through the suffering of surgery to be able to wear a bikini?

JEAN: Not for one minute. But I don't wear a bikini anyway because I'm not a good shape for a bikini. I don't taper enough

157

at the middle to look graceful and besides I don't think anyone over twenty-three should really wear a bikini.

VIRGINIA: Do you think wearing a bikini is chiefly a question of age or of figure?

JEAN: I think both are involved. A young person with a bad figure really shouldn't be wearing a bikini. There's nothing more distressing than a woman, even a very young one, spilling out over her bikini in all directions. But I think there are very, very few women past the middle twenties whose bodies are taut and tight and lithe enough to get away with a bikini.

VIRGINIA: This is going to come as a shock to my readers if they know my point of view about these things, but when I visited my daughter Lynn at the seashore last summer I saw any number of women in their forties and early fifties who were absolutely magnificent. Jean, their bodies were as lithe and slim and beautiful as you would possibly want. They weren't wearing the most abbreviated bikini, which is hardly more than two threads, but their bikinis were teensy enough to be a terrible challenge and they came through beautifully. I agree with you that a bikini is vulgar when there is any fat at all. But I feel it is less a question of age than of figure perfection.

JEAN: That's true enough—but how many women in their forties and fifties have 100 percent fat-free bodies?

VIRGINIA: I've seen more than I would have believed possible. The thing I worry about though is the sexual drive that makes some women go about changing their features. If she thinks she will suddenly become physically attractive to a man and be the sex symbol of the neighborhood just because her nostrils have been shortened, I think this is a woman who needs psychiatry more than plastic surgery. Of course if the surgery gives her poise and helps her to feel more secure and freed from what she viewed as a deformity, then it's all well and good. There's a member of our family who at sixteen didn't have that bad a nose but wanted it changed. She didn't look all that different after the surgery, yet she is like a bird out of a cage. She's never been so happy.

JEAN: I know a woman past forty who had her nose straightened and shortened. It wasn't in any sense a terrible or deformed nose to begin with. Nobody meeting her would ever have thought, "Why doesn't she *do* something about that nose?" But she'd suffered all her life and when her husband became prosperous, the first thing she did was to have her nose bobbed, against the advice of all her friends and relatives. It was the most amazing thing. After the surgery she began to act like a great beauty. She came into a room holding her head up with an air of great presence. She bought new clothes. She took care of her figure. She became a whole new personality and a nicer personality, too. She was kinder and more concerned about other people because she'd stopped brooding about herself. If plastic surgery works that way, I'm all for it.

VIRGINIA: Unfortunately, it doesn't work all the time. I've seen it go the opposite way. One woman after surgery became so preoccupied with herself that she turned into a complete bore. That's why I think there has to be a strong psychological evaluation before surgery to find out what it is you're really looking for. I think anyone would like to look prettier. I don't think there's anything too vain about wanting to be prettier. But if your drive goes beyond that, you should question your motives. And the indiscriminate desire to re-create the past through plastic surgery is something that worries me because a personality change does go on and must go on through all the phases of a woman's life. And if through surgery her appearance gets out of step with her personality, I think she's going to have emotional trouble.

Another thing, there's a certain loveliness that comes in the face of a woman who is not trying so desperately. Think of the terrible look you see on the faces of women who have married much younger men. Do you know that the minute such a woman sees a younger woman enter the room, she takes out her compact.

JEAN: "Taking out her compact" reminds me. In your autobiography you said that Zsa Zsa Gabor was the only woman you know who has achieved such perfection that she can take out a compact, study herself in the mirror, and close the compact without doing a thing. Well, the other night seated in my line of vision at a restaurant was a young woman, not pretty but very chic-looking, very contemporary. She was having dinner with a man. I would say that on an average of every five minutes she had that compact out. Luckily there were two couples at our table—if I had been alone with my husband he wouldn't have been that interested. The other woman and I began keeping score. We poked each other every time that compact came out. You'll have to believe me that we were both black and blue by the time dessert was served. What do you make of that, Virginia?

VIRGINIA: I'd say that she'd just changed her hair style or her hair color or done something new that she couldn't get used to. Maybe she'd just had surgery. Whatever it was, she was like a child with a new toy.

JEAN: I'd say that's a very generous explanation you've offered. I don't think I'd be so understanding.

VIRGINIA: Well, it is an obnoxious and boring thing to see a woman with her nose constantly buried in her compact.

Now I think it's time to give you some basic medical facts about plastic surgery and for these authentic details I went to my good friend Dr. Lester L. Coleman, the renowned otolaryngologist, whose interest in the psychological aspects of plastic surgery is well known to the readers of his book, *Freedom from Fear,* and his nationally syndicated medical column, "Speaking of Your Health."

VIRGINIA: Tell me, Doctor, is plastic surgery safe?

DR. COLEMAN: When performed by a qualified surgeon who is well trained in this specialty, plastic surgery is remarkably safe. Most of the operations are performed on basically healthy people. Even so, surgeons take into consideration all the factors of risk that are involved in any kind of surgery.

VIRGINIA: When a person is contemplating a plastic operation, how can he find a reliable, well-trained surgeon in the community?

DR. COLEMAN: The family physician in general practice is always the most dependable person to direct anyone to a competent specialist in any field of medicine. He knows the training, accomplishments, and hospital position of the plastic surgeons who are available in his and other communities.

Patients are sometimes embarrassed to discuss their desire for plastic surgery with their own doctors. This is difficult to understand because there is no shame or stigma in wanting to become more attractive. Unfortunately, patients sometimes pay a penalty for not taking advantage of the judgment of their doctors in this important decision.

The local Medical Society found in most large cities and in all states is an excellent source of reference for a list of highly qualified surgeons. The administrator of a hospital can supply the names of plastic surgeons on his staff.

By these means patients can ensure themselves that the plastic surgeon they select is well equipped to handle not only their physical needs before, during, and after surgery, but any emotional problems that may be associated with the operation.

VIRGINIA: What are the types of plastic surgery?

DR. COLEMAN: You must remember that cosmetic surgery is one phase of plastic surgery. A great many operations are done for rehabilitation of the handicapped and for those disfigured by severe burns or injuries. Much of the progress in plastic surgery has developed out of the wars we have engaged in. As for the most frequent types of cosmetic surgery, they include: the nasal plastic which involves reshaping of the nose; the eye plastic in which bags, wrinkles, and lines around the eyes are removed; the facial or neck plastic which deletes wrinkles and excess flabbiness in the face or neck; the breast plastic which changes the contour of the breasts to make them smaller or larger.

VIRGINIA: Doctor, do you think people who want plastic surgery should be encouraged or discouraged in their desire?

DR. COLEMAN: That would depend largely on their motive. If someone in the theater or public eye wants to maintain his image in order to prolong his livelihood, certainly he should be encouraged. I don't think anyone should be discouraged from having any plastic procedure done if it will bring him or her the specific joy or personal happiness he or she thinks it will.

But there is a very distinct warning I must sound. There are people who seek under the guise of plastic surgery a new social, marital, economic, professional, or sexual rebirth. When plastic surgery is done on those who do not come face to face with their own *real* reasons, the operation is fraught with the danger of disappointment. For no matter how successful the operation is anatomically, the patient will be disappointed because he does not have the rebirth he seeks.

VIRGINIA: Does such a patient turn his anger against the surgeon?

DR. COLEMAN: He may do that, or he may be in great psychological trouble. Look at it this way—if his bad nose is turned into an excellent nose, yet he still remains unfulfilled, he has been cheated of his single most satisfactory excuse for his personal failure.

VIRGINIA: How can anyone avoid such a pitfall?

DR. COLEMAN: The patient and his doctor should discuss freely exactly what the operation is, why it is wanted, how much of what is wanted will be achieved, what it will cost, whether it will be covered by medical insurance. If the doctor suspects any kind of emotional problem, he should insist upon a psychological evaluation, in the same way that he would ask for a blood or X-ray study to help him in his judgment.

VIRGINIA: Let me ask some of those questions now. What about cost?

DR. COLEMAN: All I can say is that cosmetic surgery is not cheap. Fees will vary from the hundreds to the thousands of dollars depending on the man who does the surgery, his position, training, the type of operation, the time it will take. You should know that there are qualified surgeons all over America who will reduce their fees for people who truly need but can't afford a cosmetic operation.

VIRGINIA: How long will the benefits of an operation last?

DR. COLEMAN: You must understand that surgery of the face, eye, neck, and breast is aimed at undoing the progressive changes that occur with growing older. Since the aging process continues after surgery, changes will occur even in the tissues helped by the operation. In general, I would say that five years is a good average time to expect benefits to last. Often it's longer, rarely shorter. Of course the surgery can be repeated, and usually the second or third time it is simpler and less extensive. Surgery of the nose and ear, which is concerned with basic structure, rarely changes to any perceptible degree over the years.

VIRGINIA: Is there any pain?

DR. COLEMAN: Remarkably little and what there is can be easily controlled during and after surgery.

VIRGINIA: How long does it take?

DR. COLEMAN: The doctor will have to tell you in each case. The operation itself is over quickly. But the recovery time, until everything is healed and all discoloration has disappeared, is highly individual.

VIRGINIA: What about skin scrapings and peelings?

DR. COLEMAN: There are limitless numbers of quackeries and exploitative techniques that appeal to those who want an easier and less expensive way out. These include burning and freezing and peeling with caustic acids by unskilled people without medical training. I must tell you they are filled with danger and can leave physical and emotional scars from which the patient rarely recovers.

I think Dr. Coleman has made the whole plastic-surgery picture clearer for all of us. And I will say to readers: If you are considering plastic surgery, you must really examine yourself inside and out and never forget that the only thing the surgeon can change is your anatomy, not your psyche.

22

Behind the Scenes

Virginia, this is Jean telling you (and our readers) about something that is going on behind your back. You know that when you tape your "Girl Talk" programs every Thursday and Friday your guests repair briefly to the makeup room up a short flight of stairs from the TV stage to have their hair arranged and their makeup applied before going on camera. You, of course, don't see any of this procedure because you are in your own dressing room, changing your clothes and getting briefed for the "Girl Talk" interview that is about to be filmed.

Don't Blame the Mirror

Well, I've been hanging around backstage, looking over the shoulders of your guests as they are being made up and chatting with them about their particular beauty problems. I suppose women talk more freely when you catch them with their skin stripped down to the naked pores. At any rate, I've picked up some little-known beauty thoughts from some well-known personalities, while Bert Roth, the ABC-Paramount makeup artist was working his artistry on their faces.

First, a word or two about Bert, who began as a portrait photographer but fourteen years ago became so interested in makeup and the effects to be achieved with makeup that he changed careers. For "Girl Talk" guests he does an extremely natural makeup that can easily be worn into the street after the program. He says, "Whenever a woman's makeup deviates from a natural look, she's in trouble. Startling, dramatic effects are all right for a pretty model whose business it is to be noticed. But the average woman should not exaggerate even a good thing. Take false eyelashes. They're a wonderful addition to a woman's beauty wardrobe, but not when she piles on three pairs of mink lashes and looks like a furry animal."

Roth warns against using too much light-tone eyeshadow just below the eyebrow. "In stage makeup we highlight the bone under the brow to create the illusion of aging. A prominent bone under the brow is characteristic of old people. Don't age yourself through mistaken use of a highlight on the bone."

The wingtip of eyeliner extended outward beyond the eyelid by many women does not meet with Roth's approval. It is fine on eyes that naturally have a doe look and an upward slant and it works well on young girls. But a woman who has large eyes, or who has lines in the lids or a fold at the corner of the eyes, should avoid this extension of the liner because it accents any

166

crepiness that might be present. What's more, if it is not applied in precisely the right place it can give a despondent droop to the eyes. Most women, he feels, should contour their eyeliner only as far as the outward corner of the eye.

Roth belongs to the school that selects lipstick primarily by clothing color—an orange-toned lipstick with browns and greens, a pink lipstick with blues, a clear red with red. He is enormously impressed with the makeup skill and self-knowledge most women of the stage and in public life have acquired. But even a professional woman occasionally gives him a bad time. A fledgling off-Broadway actress who had won splendid reviews in a difficult role was making her first "Girl Talk" appearance. He was horrified at her makeup. She wore a whitened beige foundation and powder which gave her skin the color and texture of uncooked bread, great black circles painted under and over her eyes, and lipstick the color of faded nylon. Bert's first thought was that she was terribly ill and he should call an ambulance. But she was feeling fine and didn't even want him to bother with her face. "I made up at home," she explained matter of factly. He pointed out that TV makeup is different from street makeup—a tactful lie, for most guests go right from the camera to the street looking marvelous.

When Bert finally finished with her, she was a different girl. He used a peach-tinted foundation to give life to her sallow skin, a touch of brown on the bone over each eye to make it less noticeable, a bit of brown the length of her nose to diminish it. He gave her a fine line of dark brown just over the lashes, a little turquoise shadow on the lids and a good deal of mascara on her lashes to thicken and lengthen them. Then he used a full-toned coral lipstick. The effect to me and all the rest of us backstage was instant recovery from a wasting disease. But do you know that before she left the studio to go home that headstrong girl took off every bit of Bert's makeup and redid her face in deathbed style?

Now for a look at some of the girls at the makeup table.

Cindy Adams, the wife of comic Joey Adams and biographer of Indonesia's Sukarno, has perfect ivory skin and black, black hair. She began using false eyelashes when she was fifteen and puts them on today as automatically as eyeglasses, using the deftest flick of her fingers you ever saw and surgical glue. Believe it or not, she uses only Noxema on her skin as a foundation, then applies cake powder. She arrived for the show completely made up, asked Bert only to emphasize her hairline at each side of her brow with black pancake makeup.

Carol Bruce, the singer and actress, gives the impression of being taller than she is by her magnificent carriage. She is especially proud of the makeup job she does on her eyebrows. First she outlines the full brows using a plastic stencil to get the inner curve of the brow just right. Then she does the rest freehand, filling in the stencil outline with the tiniest of pencil strokes. She uses black eyeliner and false lashes for the stage. For the street she thinks a dark-brown liner is dark enough for anyone except a Spanish dancer with blueblack hair and black eyes. She emphasizes the dimple in her chin with a spot of dark makeup and shapes her jawline with a darker shade of foundation than she uses on the rest of her face.

Carol was grateful to Maria Stevens, the "Girl Talk" hairdresser, for the suggestion that she try a touch of wax to keep the tiny unruly hairs at the back of her neck in a neat upsweep. Carol had been using spray, but the minute she tried the wax she was delighted with it. (Ask your druggist for moustache wax.)

Behind the Scenes

A word about Maria, who has been doing stage, Hollywood, and TV hair styling for longer than she would like to talk about. Maria has authoritative hands that make hair behave by barely fluttering over it. She seems to be able to persuade an unruly lock to lie down docilely merely by stroking it once or twice. Maria has this to say: "I'm always amazed at how much the real pros respect the hairdresser. Actresses usually arrive on the program with beautifully arranged hair styled just right for them, but they say to me, 'Maria, if you think it needs a little more height or should be a little smoother, just take care of it.'

"But the nonpros, the women who've never been on TV or the stage, are different. So many of them don't want me to touch their hair. 'That's the way I wear it,' they say. There's always defiance in their voice. They just love their hair straggly, or lank, or in a great bush. I always wish I could get my hands on the hair they won't let me touch. I could do so much for those girls."

Gwen Verdon, the fabulous dancer who made a hit of the show *Sweet Charity*, is always in a hurry and has had to learn to work very fast. She is one of the very few women in the theater who does not believe in a lipstick brush. She gets a perfect outline using the sharp edge of a lipstick applied directly from the stick. "Why do they make it in a stick if it isn't meant to be put on that way?" she asks. Gwen uses any dark-brown or black eyeliner that happens to be at hand—pencil, liquid, or black pancake. (That's a trick they learn on stage—to apply black pancake with an eyeliner brush for a strong, definite line.) Gwen always wears blue shadow to reflect her blue eyes.

A young magazine writer arrived to go on the program, a girl with no makeup and a face as round as a full moon. "Would you like me to take five pounds off your face?" asked the makeup man. (It was not Bert that day—he was on vacation.) The writer nodded indifferently. *She* knew the only way to take poundage off her face was to stop eating. I watched fascinated as the makeup man applied foundation in an S-shaped line from the girl's temple to the high point of her cheekbone down to her jawline. He did this on both sides. Then he used on her forehead and on the center of her face between the two S-lines a cake makeup one tone darker than her natural skin tone. He filled in behind the S-line with one tone darker than that. Under her eyes and in the furrows from the corner of her nose to her mouth he used one tone lighter than the first foundation he had applied. (That meant he was using three shades of foundation— the lightest under her eyes, the next darker in the center of her face, the darkest at the outer part of that moonlike face.)

I can tell you this—there wasn't any blood, but there sure had been surgery. That girl sat up so tall in her chair to see what was going on and leaned so close to the mirror to analyze what had happened that I thought she was going right through the glass. Yes, the five pounds were gone, the face was an altogether different shape, and she was writing down in her notebook exactly what the makeup man had done to her face, step by step and shade by shade. I'm afraid she's never going on that diet.

Geneviève—do you remember when she was on TV almost nightly? She's still the same effervescent personality with a French accent so enchanting that you find yourself unconsciously adopting it when you speak to her. Geneviève turned up for "Girl Talk" in a beige suede pants suit made for her in Spain. The suede fitted her compact figure as delightfully as it did the antelope who originally wore the skins. Geneviève is a water girl. "Theenk about water," she said, "eet ees fantastic. You cook een eet, wash een eet, refresh yourself een eet. Zome peo-

170

ple even dreenk eet." She shuddered delicately. "My dog was cured weeth eet."

"Did your dog go on a water diet?" I asked.

"Oh, no—he sweem een eet."

Geneviève herself swims in it, steams her face in it, bathes in it. She applies no makeup in the morning, but gives her face a good creaming when she rises. About noon her skin gets a washing with soap and water and a soft brush. If she is going out she makes up—usually with panstick, passes the panstick right over her eyebrows to lighten them and applies lipstick without a brush.

"You can say again I love water," she called back to me as she skipped down the stairs in that pert pants suit with matching visored cap. "But I don't dreenk eet—nevair!"

Lucille Ball, the beloved star of "I Love Lucy," appeared on "Girl Talk" recently as a solo guest to discuss her home, her children, her career, and some of the problems of being one of the busiest women in the world. "I can darn, mend, cook, plant, and clean a house pretty good, but I can't sew," she began in a breezy, friendly voice. She was wearing a beige flannel suit with white collar and white blouse. Her red hair was swept high. Her skin, close up and under strong lights, was as satiny as a child's. "I use steam on my face, I love it. I soak a Turkish towel in hot water and hold it to my skin. I add soap if my face needs washing. I can feel the pores opening as that heat penetrates. I don't bother to close the pores—I let them do that themselves."

Lucille never leaves cream on for more than five minutes. Offstage she uses no base, just a flick of powder. Lipstick goes on with a brush to shape the outline of that famous mouth. She uses two shades of lipstick—darker underneath and extend-

171

ing beyond the natural lipline, lighter on top for gloss and high-light. She pencils in her eyebrows hair by hair to achieve the desired effect.

Lucille is in love with brushes. She goes to art stores and buys them in all sizes, shapes, and contours and then experiments before the mirror to see which brush gives the best results on eyebrows, eyelashes, lips, stroking down powder, blending eyeshadow.

On that glowing hair she uses real, old-fashioned henna. "People laugh when I say I use henna, the youngsters don't even know what it is. If you're that young I'll tell you—it was the original hair color for redheads, and I think it's made from the leaves of a plant. Now I don't use it for color. I get color in two stages, first with a lightener combined with color, then with a toner. I use the henna at the end to give my hair a life and a gleam I can't get any other way. Do you know where I'm going now? I'm exhausted, but I've got six more hours ahead of me, so it's back to my hotel to steam my face." Lucille Ball leaves the impression she thinks the world would be a better place if more people drenched their face in steam more often. She might very well be right.

If you're old enough *not* to wear a bikini, you'll remember Harriet Nelson from the dear, departed days of radio as half of the Ozzie and Harriet team. If you're young enough for a mini-skirt no bigger than a guest towel, you'll know her as Ricky Nelson's mother. Either way, she looks so smart and slim and self-possessed—like the prettiest den mother you ever saw—that I couldn't resist asking her how a woman who sees the years flying by can adjust herself to accept the evidences of time when she looks in the mirror.

172

Harriet laughed. "You forget that nature very considerately takes care of that problem for nearly all of us. If you can't stand what you see in the mirror, it's simple. Just look without your glasses!"

173

K

Reprise

Well, now the question of what beauty is has been discussed once again. I suppose that from time immemorial, from the time Eve saw her reflection in water, which must have been the first mirror, there has been a new dawn every year in the cosmetic world of beauty. Come to think of it, her name shouldn't have been Eve, it should have been Dawn, for she was the beginning of everything. I think it is so exciting to be a woman.

If I were to choose the era in which I would want to live, I very often think that figurewise, for I am curvaceous, I would

174

like to have lived at the end of the nineteenth century. But the twentieth-century woman—the mid-twentieth-century woman— has become emancipated as far as she herself is concerned. I always believe that inhibitions are not imposed by society but by the people who live in society and accept them. When prohibition came along people revolted and the speakeasy resulted.

I think if there ever were a restriction on cosmetics, the bootlegging would be the largest of any industry in the world. Women today could be forced to give up almost anything sooner than the marvelous magic of cosmetic beauty. Beauty may be only skin deep in terms of layers of skin, but psychologically it is endless and the wonders of self-interest, of cleanliness, of good grooming are as miraculous as the sunset, as exciting as the sunrise, because with each day you become a new You. The potential of a woman is something she herself has not fully realized.

Beauty is the way a woman walks, the way she thinks, the way she feels, and what she does to herself.

Now I don't want you to tell me that you're too busy or too tired or that you don't have the money to take proper care of yourself. Because if you do, I am going to ask you a question. I am going to ask you how much you spend a year on laundry for your family's clothing and your household linen, how much you spend on dry cleaning, how much you spend on a cleaning woman, how much on waxes and polishes and detergents, how much for floor polishing and window washing and rug cleaning, how much for new slipcovers, draperies, reupholstery. How much not only in money, but in time, energy, and your attention. And when you've totaled up the whole, horrendous sum for cleaning and maintenance, I'm going to hurl that amount right back at you and say to you:

Don't Blame the Mirror

"What! You spend all that to take care of *things*—mere things that can always be replaced! And for your own face, your hair, your skin, your good looks—all utterly irreplaceable, all gone for good and ever once they're gone—you don't have the time or the interest or the money! I never heard of anything so ridiculous, so destructive in all my life!"

And so for the hundredth time in this book, I say, "Don't blame the mirror!" The problem isn't there and neither is the solution.

You are the problem and you have the answer. And I think now you are going to do something about yourself.

I know you'll succeed.